Emergency First Aid For Your Dog

Handbook

Dr. Tamara S. Shearer
Edited by Stanford Apseloff

OHIO DISTINCTIVE PUBLISHING
Columbus, Ohio

Ohio Distinctive Publishing, Inc.
6500 Fiesta Drive, Columbus OH 43235
www.ohio-distinctive.com

Printed in the United States of America.

10 09 08 07 06   10 9 8 7 6 5 4 3 2

Illustrations by Claudia Beth Sheets
Cover photograph by Stanford Apseloff

ISBN: 0-9647934-4-X

Library of Congress Control Number: 2004101713

TABLE OF CONTENTS

GETTING STARTED

SPECIAL COMMENTS

This book is a first-aid guide for common emergencies. It is meant to be used as an aid when immediate veterinary care is unavailable. This book should not be used as a substitute for veterinary care. Because your veterinarian will be able to advise you best based on the particular circumstances of your dog's emergency, you should contact your veterinarian at the earliest possible moment, preferably before initiating any nonessential treatment.

PREVENTION

The reasonable precautions outlined below should decrease the risk of an emergency and may save your dog's life.

I.   Accident-Proofing Your Home

A.   Keep telephone cords, drapery cords and electrical cords out of reach.

B.   Make sure that any dog toys are sufficiently large and indestructible that they do not pose a risk of choking. Also, make sure that they do not contain any string or yarn.

C.   Make sure that your dog does not have access to socks, hose or shoes/shoelaces.

D.   Do not decorate a Christmas tree with tinsel.

E.   Keep all utensils, foils, wraps, scrub pads, etc. that may contain food smells out of reach of your dog.

F.   Never give your dog human medications of any kind without specific instructions from a veterinarian. Keep all medications out of your dog's reach.

G.   Identify and remove toxic plants and flowers.

H.   Keep your dog off of lawns that have been recently treated with pesticides or fertilizers.

I.   Keep your dog out of rooms where you have recently sprayed indoor insecticides.

J.   Never use snail bait, rat poison or poisonous ant traps.

K.   Never use continual-release toilet disinfectants.

L.   Keep windows above the ground floor at least partially closed.

M. Provide good ventilation during hot summer months.

N. Keep all trash containers covered, and keep any and all table scraps, especially bones, away from your dog.

II. Prevention for Outside the Home

A. Provide your dog with an identification tag, but make sure that the tag is not dangling and in danger of catching on anything.

B. Make sure that your dog's collar fits properly, and with puppies check the fit frequently because they grow quickly.

C. Use a breakaway dog collar to prevent accidental strangulation.

D. Properly dispose of antifreeze.

E. Never use snail bait or rat poison.

F. Do not leave your dog outside unsupervised.

G. Honk your car horn before pulling out of the driveway.

H. Identify and remove toxic plants/flowers. Keep your dog away from grass that was recently treated with any yard chemicals.

I. In the winter, provide fresh water, and change it before it freezes.

J. In cool months, provide dry, draft-free shelter. The shelter should be just big enough for the dog to lie down and to stand; too much height, depth and length does not promote heat conservation and will not serve well as a shelter. Put bedding (i.e., clean, dry straw) in the shelter.

K. During hot summer months, provide well-ventilated shelter and extra drinking water. Overheating can lead to heat stroke.

III. Preventive Medicine

A. Keep vaccinations and physical exams up-to-date.

B. Get an annual heartworm test and heartworm preventive medicine.

C. Follow flea-product instructions carefully.

D. Never give any medication without a veterinarian's advice.

E. Never give your dog any people medications unless directed by your veterinarian. People medications can be deadly to dogs.

F. Spay or neuter your dog.

IV. Additional Measures

A. Never leave a dog alone for an extended period of time.

B. Never leave a dog alone in a hot car with the windows up.

C. Keep hair coat free of mats (to prevent skin sores).

D. Keep paws free of ice, mud and salt; wash and dry the paws.

E. Never call your dog to come if the dog has to cross a road in front of cars. Instead, cross the street yourself, and then bring the dog to the other side with you.

V. Preventive Nutrition

A. Never feed dogs cat food. Cat food lacks the balance of nutrients essential for healthy dogs. Also, it may cause diarrhea, or the high fat content may promote obesity.

B. Never feed dogs milk. Milk can cause digestive problems, such as diarrhea.

C. Do not supplement diets without a veterinarian's advice. Wrong supplementation can cause urinary tract problems, metabolic problems and even mineralization of the kidneys.

D. Never feed a dog raw fish. Raw fish causes a thiamine deficiency which may result in loss of appetite, a hunched and painful stance and possibly convulsions. Even if it is cooked, never feed a dog a diet of fish exclusively.

E. Never feed a dog foods that contain rancid fats or excess polyunsaturated fats, because they can cause a vitamin E deficiency leading to a variety of muscle diseases.

F. Never feed your dog table scraps, bones or chocolates.

G. Never oversupplement your dog's diet with vitamin D or fish liver oil. Excess can cause bone disease as well as digestive upset.

THE FIRST-AID KIT

Having a good first-aid kit is critical when dealing with a pet emergency. Use the following outline to prepare your first-aid kit.

I. First-Aid Box

A. Obtain a box that is
   (1) Transportable (shoe-box size, preferably with a handle)
   (2) Durable and water-resistant (like a fishing tackle box)
   (3) Nonlocking (to provide easy access).

B. Label the outside of the box "DOG FIRST AID."

C. Store the first-aid box in plain view.

II. First-Aid Provisions (to put into First-Aid Box)

A. 2 rolls of 3" gauze bandage

B. 12 gauze sponges 3"x 3"

C. Nonstick adhesive tape

D. Nonstick bandages

E. Antibiotic ointment (e.g., Polysporin®) – small tube

F. Water-soluble lubricating jelly (e.g., K-Y™ Brand)

G. Saline solution – 8 ounces (same as used for contact-lens care)

H. Hydrogen peroxide – 8 ounces
I. Alcohol
J. Eyedropper or dosage syringe
K. Tweezers
L. Scissors
M. Nail trimmers
N. Rectal thermometer
O. Muzzle – preferably nylon
P. Benadryl® or diphenhydramine elixir (12.5 mg per 5 ml liquid)
Q. Paper towels – to clean up any mess
R. Emergency information (see below)

III. Emergency Information
A. Emergency telephone numbers:
    (1) Poison control _____
        The ASPCA Animal Poison Control Center provides
        assistance for a fee – $50 at the time of this printing:
        1-800-548-2423.
    (2) Veterinarians _____
        _____
    (3) After-hours veterinarians_____
        _____
    (4) Fire department _____
B. A copy of this book
C. A plant identification book

IV. Additional First-Aid Items
A. Towels – for use in restraining your dog
B. Blanket – to keep your dog warm and comfortable
C. Pet carrier – for transport if you have a small dog
D. A plywood board cut to the appropriate size for your dog and
    for your car – to carry your injured dog safely to the car
E. Two 2-liter soda bottles – for use as hot-water bottles
F. Elizabethan collar – see page 21.

HOW TO APPROACH AN EMERGENCY

Regardless of the emergency, there are some basic steps you
can take to help your dog. The following information should enable
you to take appropriate action in a variety of emergency situations.

I. **Basic Steps in Emergency Care**
A. Stay calm. Assess dangers surrounding the situation. Use common sense during the crisis. If you are unable to deal with the situation, then delegate the emergency care to someone else.
B. Observe the urgency. Does the emergency appear to be mild, moderate or severe? Evaluate whether the situation is getting better, staying the same or getting worse.
C. Seek assistance:
    (1) Call the dog's doctor. If the emergency occurs outside of regular veterinary hours, call for after-hour help.
    (2) If you suspect poisoning and cannot reach a veterinarian, call your local poison control hotline or the national ASPCA Animal Poison Control Center. (The ASPCA Animal Poison Control Center provides assistance for a fee – $50 at the time of this printing: 1-800-548-2423.)

II. **First-Aid Instructions**
A. Identify the problem; then refer to the alphabetically arranged emergency section or to the index of this book.
B. If the problem cannot be identified, follow these steps:
    (1) Confine the dog.
    (2) Keep the dog quiet and warm.
    (3) Note any and all symptoms.
    (4) Observe whether the condition is getting better, staying the same or getting worse.
C. Contact a veterinarian as soon as possible.

RESTRAINT

If you follow the rules for basic restraint techniques, the stress during an emergency will be decreased for the pet and for you.

I. **Behavioral Changes Affecting Restraint of the Sick, Hurt Dog**
A. Listless or depressed dogs may be easier to handle.
B. Hurt or sick dogs may become anxious or aggressive and be more difficult to handle. They may bite.

II. **Approaching an Injured Dog**
A. Talk to the dog calmly and quietly.
B. Move toward the dog slowly.
C. Do not chase the dog.

III. Restraining the Injured Dog

A. Obtain a towel (for a small dog) or blanket (for a large dog) and a muzzle.

B. Approach from behind to help prevent getting bitten.

C. If the dog is trying to bite, use a muzzle, unless the dog is having trouble breathing or has been vomiting. Never muzzle a pet that is having breathing difficulty or is nauseated! Do not use a muzzle if your dog has a flat face (e.g., a pug, boxer, English bulldog, etc.). See page 20.

   Caution: dogs can bite through virtually any gloves, and even a friendly dog may bite when it is injured!

D. Place the towel or blanket over the dog.

E. Gather the dog in the towel or blanket to complete the restraint.

F. To carry or transport the dog, see Transportation, pages 11-14.

TRANSPORTATION

It is important to note that the dog's condition will dictate the specific procedures that you will need to use for safe transport. The outline that follows is a guide to transport under a variety of emergency conditions.

I. Equipment Needed in Transportation

A. Pet carrier (if you have a small dog)

B. Towels

C. Blanket

D. 2-liter soda bottle filled with warm water

E.   Muzzle

F.   Collar and leash

G.   Car safety belt for dogs (optional)

H.   Plywood board cut to fit your dog and your car

II.   Carrying an Injured Dog

A.   Even a friendly dog may bite when in pain. Therefore, apply a muzzle if the dog is not having difficulty breathing and has not been vomiting. Do not use a muzzle if your dog has a flat face (e.g., a pug, boxer, English bulldog, etc.). See page 20.

B.   **For a small dog:**

    (1) Obtain a pet carrier that has a removable top. If a pet carrier is not available, use a corrugated cardboard box of an appropriate size. A carrier or box that opens at the top rather than the side is preferable because the dog can be put in and taken out without pushing or pulling the pet.

    (2) Slide your hands under the dog to lift the pet. Take care to support the dog's entire body as you lift and place the dog into the carrier.

    (3) Place towels around the dog to keep the pet from sliding in the pet carrier.

C.   **For a medium-size or large dog:**

    (1) For spinal cord injuries, there is risk of additional injury from moving the dog. The ideal carrying method is to slide the dog onto a plywood board and then secure the pet with a blanket. You will need someone to assist you in carrying the board. Make sure the board will fit in the vehicle you plan to use for transport.

    (2) For emergencies other than spinal cord injuries, you may still need to use a board (as detailed immediately above) if the dog is too large for you to carry by yourself. If the dog is not too large for you to carry by yourself, place one arm under the dog's stomach (below the ribs) and the other hand under the dog's neck (with the dog's neck in the corner of your elbow). See the illustration on page 11. When lifting the dog, bend your knees and lift with equal pressure on both arms.

III.   Transporting a Dog in Stable Condition

A.   For your own driving safety:

    (1) The dog should ride in the seat next to the driver or in the back, and never in the driver's lap or near the pedals.

    (2) Restrain and secure the pet with a leash or a special dog

safety belt, or, for a small dog, you may have a helper hold the pet.
B. For your dog's safety:
(1) Never allow the pet to ride with its head outside the window or with its paws on the window's edge.
(2) Never allow a small dog to ride on the back window ledge.
(3) Never drive with your dog in the open bed of a truck.

IV. Transporting a Dog in Shock
A. If the dog is in pain, you may wish to use a muzzle. However, use a muzzle only if the dog is not having difficulty breathing and has not been vomiting. If at any time the dog has difficulty breathing, remove the muzzle. Also, do not use a muzzle if your dog has a flat face (e.g., a pug, boxer, English bulldog, etc.).
B. Lay the dog on the seat of the car. Pack blankets around the dog to keep the pet warm. If you are concerned that the dog may slide off of the seat onto the floor, pack the floor area with a pillow or blankets. Place one or two 2-liter soda bottles filled with warm water (not hot water) against the dog. See illustrations on page 80.

V. Transporting a Dog with Fractures or Back Injuries
A. Because fractures are painful, you may wish to use a muzzle to prevent being bitten when you move your dog. However, use a muzzle only if the dog is not having difficulty breathing and has not been vomiting. If at any time the dog has difficulty breathing, remove the muzzle. Also, do not use a muzzle if your dog has a flat face (e.g., a pug, boxer, English bulldog, etc.).
B. Plan the transport to minimize movement of the dog. For a fractured leg, you might want to fold a newspaper to make a splint to support the leg. Keep the fractured leg up.
C. **For a small dog:**
(1) Obtain a pet carrier that has a removable top. If a pet carrier is not available, use a corrugated cardboard box of an appropriate size. A carrier or box that opens at the top rather than the side is preferable because the dog can be put in and taken out without pushing or pulling the pet.
(2) Slide your hands under the dog to lift the pet. Take care to support the dog's entire body as you lift. Place the dog into the carrier with its injured side up, if possible.
(3) Place towels around the dog to keep the pet from sliding in the carrier. Place a 2-liter soda bottle filled with warm water (not hot water) against the dog. See illustration on page 80.

13

D. **For a medium-size or large dog:**
    (1) Obtain a plywood board that will fit easily into your car to use as a stretcher. Slide the dog onto the board, taking care to move the pet as little as possible. If a board is not available, you may use a blanket or towel as a stretcher instead, but the board is highly preferable because it will result in less movement of the pet and therefore less chance of aggravating the injury.
    (2) Ideally, place the plywood board with the dog on it into your vehicle. If the board will not fit, slide the dog off of the board and onto the seat with as little movement of the pet as possible. If you have used a blanket or towel rather than a board, keep the blanket or towel under the dog when you put the pet into the car.
    (3) Pack blankets around the dog to keep the pet warm. If you think the dog may slide off of the seat onto the floor, pack the floor area with a pillow or blankets. Place one or two 2-liter soda bottles filled with warm water (not hot water) against the dog. See illustrations on page 80.

SPECIAL CONSIDERATIONS

"Special considerations" refers to conditions that may complicate emergency treatment. In particular, this chapter will address the special needs of puppies, older dogs and dogs with preexisting diseases or medical conditions. Because each dog has unique characteristics, you should consult your veterinarian regarding any special treatment or special considerations in the day-to-day care of your pet as well as in emergency situations.

Because of the vast number of special considerations and the unique characteristics of each dog, this chapter can only begin to address the particular needs of your pet. If you suspect that your dog has special needs, find out now before an emergency develops so that you can administer the best possible care for your pet.

I. **Puppies**
A. Because of a puppy's small body size, it has little reserve to support itself during an illness.
B. Puppies have immature immune systems that are inadequate for fighting infections after the puppies are weaned from their mothers. Make sure your puppy gets timely vaccinations.

C. Because of a puppy's curiosity, it is prone to finding trouble that can result in injury.

II. Older Dogs

A. Older dogs require special care because their organs/internal functions may be diseased or show aging changes, making them more sensitive to disease processes.

B. Make sure older dogs have easy access to food and water.

C. Some older dogs are prone to becoming underweight; therefore, they have less body reserve than fit dogs.

D. Other older dogs are overweight, which can predispose them to diseases and slow their recoveries.

E. Dogs over five years of age should have blood tests and checkups twice each year to screen for early diseases of the internal organs, diabetes and anemias. X-rays and an EKG may be warranted to identify early heart disease.

III. Preexisting Diseases

A. Obesity may predispose a dog to early heart, liver and kidney disease. It may also cause problems with early arthritis.

B. Metabolic disease problems (e.g., thyroid disorders, diabetes, hypoadrenocorticism) can complicate recoveries if the diseases are not properly diagnosed and treated.

C. Heartworm disease may debilitate a dog and lead to chronic fatigue and heart and liver failure. The dog's weakened condition may make any emergency more urgent and may slow any recovery from illness or injury.

D. Other parasitic diseases (e.g., worms and protozoa) can weaken your dog and make any emergency even more critical.

IV. Body Shape and Size

A. Dogs with flat faces (e.g., pug, boxer, English bulldog, etc.) may have difficulty breathing when under stress and may overheat quickly. Therefore, do not muzzle a dog that has a flat face.

B. Some dogs have underdeveloped/small nostrils (e.g., Lhaso apso, pugs, Pekinese, Shih Tzu). Never use a muzzle on these dogs.

C. Deep-chested dogs (e.g., Irish setters, Great Danes, German shepherds) may be predisposed to twisted stomach. See pages 32-33.

D. Obesity may predispose a dog to early heart, liver and kidney disease. It may also cause problems with early arthritis.

FIRST-AID TECHNIQUES

WRAPPING A WOUND

Wraps should be applied to areas where abrasions or lacerations are present to keep them clean and to prevent the dog from causing further trauma by licking a wound. In many situations where a wrap is needed, an Elizabethan collar may also be necessary. See page 21.

I. First-Aid Materials
A. Antibiotic ointment (e.g., Polysporin®)
B. Saline solution
C. Nonstick adhesive tape
D. Nonstick bandages
E. Gauze wrap

II. Technique Instructions
A. Treat the injury according to the specific instructions provided elsewhere in this book (e.g., Abrasions on page 22).
B. Apply antibiotic ointment over wound.
C. Press nonstick bandage to wound.
D. Secure nonstick bandage to wound by wrapping gauze around the leg or body. The gauze should be snug but not tight. The wrap tightness should not restrict circulation or the dog's breathing.
E. Secure the gauze by applying adhesive tape to the wrap.
F. Monitor the pet for any evidence of swelling to the limb below the wrap. If swelling occurs, the wrap is too tight and should be removed immediately. If the dog's breathing is hindered, also remove the wrap.

III. Emergency Situations Where the Technique Applies
A. Abrasions
B. Lacerations
C. Burns
D. Other skin irritations
E. Compound/open fractures

MONITORING VITAL SIGNS

NORMAL VITAL SIGNS FOR A DOG AT REST
Temperature 101 to 102.5 degrees Fahrenheit
Pulse/Heart Rate 100 to 130 beats per minute
Respiratory Rate 20 to 24 breaths per minute

The above signs are for a normal mature dog at rest. An excited dog, or one that has been running around, will have an elevated heart rate and an elevated respiratory rate. However, elevated vital signs for a dog at rest may be a sign of infection, disease, overheating or a variety of other health problems. Low vital signs may indicate that the dog is in shock.

I. First-Aid Materials
A. Rectal thermometer
B. Lubricating jelly (e.g., K-Y™ Brand) or petroleum jelly
C. Watch or clock with second hand

II. Technique Instructions
A. Taking the temperature:
    (1) Lubricate a rectal thermometer with lubricating jelly or petroleum jelly. Insert the thermometer gently into the dog's rectum approximately 1 inch.
    (2) Wait 2 minutes, and then remove and read the thermometer.
    (3) Normal temperature is 101 to 102.5 degrees Fahrenheit.
B. Taking the pulse:
    (1) Lay your hand just behind the dog's shoulder blade on either side of its chest and feel for the heart beat (as illustrated on page 19), or
    (2) Place your hand in the groin area of the dog's abdomen and feel for the femoral pulse.
    (3) Count the beats per minute (e.g., count for 15 seconds and multiply by 4).
    (4) Normal pulse at rest should be approximately 100 to 130 beats per minute. (Active pulse may be much higher.)
C. Taking respirations:
    (1) If the dog is lying quietly, watch the chest rise and fall.
    (2) Count the number of breaths the dog takes in a minute.
    (3) Normal resting respiratory rate is approximately 20 to 24 breaths per minute. (Active rate may be much higher.)

INDUCING VOMITING

When a dog ingests a poisonous substance, time is critical, and your ability to induce your dog to vomit may save its life.

NOTE: NEVER induce vomiting if a pet is unconscious, having difficulty breathing, or is in a stupor. Also never induce vomiting if there is suspicion of ingestion of petroleum distillates, acids or alkalis (e.g., kerosene, gasoline, motor oil, various household cleaning supplies). As a general rule, follow the instructions on the product warning label regarding whether to induce vomiting. If in doubt, call a poison control center, but make sure you act quickly.

I. **First-Aid Materials**
A. Hydrogen peroxide
B. Eyedropper or dosage syringe

II. **Technique Instructions**
A. First, try to contact your veterinarian. Next, induce vomiting only if the dog is conscious. To induce vomiting, feed the dog 1 teaspoon of hydrogen peroxide (mixed with 1 teaspoon of milk). For large dogs, over 60 pounds, double the dosage. If the dog will not drink the mixture or if there is no milk available, force-feed the dog the hydrogen peroxide using an eyedropper.
B. If vomiting does not occur within 10 minutes, repeat the procedure twice if needed.
C. Contact a veterinarian as soon as possible.

CARDIOPULMONARY RESUSCITATION

CPR is used to revive a dog that is not breathing and has no heartbeat (e.g., from drowning or severe electrical shock). When CPR is needed, it must be performed immediately. Therefore, you must be able to assess the need quickly and perform the technique effectively. (No special equipment or materials are needed.)

NOTE: CPR is a technique of last resort when the dog shows no signs of life. If there is any evidence that the dog is breathing, do not perform this technique.

I. **Technique Instructions**
A. Lay the dog on its side (and throughout these procedures keep the dog on its side).

B. Check for breathing by watching the dog's chest rise and fall.
C. **If the dog is breathing**, proceed no further. Do not use CPR.
D. **If the dog is not breathing**,
    (1) Establish an airway by removing any debris from the dog's mouth or by moving the tongue from the back of the throat. (See illustration below.) Check for breathing by watching the dog's chest rise and fall. If the dog is breathing, proceed no further, and do not use CPR.
    (2) Check for a pulse by placing a hand over the dog's chest just behind the shoulder blade to feel the heartbeat. (See illustration below.)
E. **If the dog still is not breathing**,
    (1) Cup your hand(s) over the dog's nose and mouth to form a seal. Deliver 2 breaths into the pet every second. If the seal is proper, you should observe the dog's chest rise and fall.
    (2) If after you have delivered 5 breaths the dog does not show signs of breathing on its own or signs of consciousness, and there is no heartbeat, have a helper place a hand just behind the dog's shoulder blades (as illustrated below), and apply gentle but firm compressions downward (compressing 1/2 to 1 inch for a small dog, up to as much as 2 inches for a large dog) at a rate of 2 compressions every second. If a helper is not available, alternate delivering 2 breaths then 15 compressions. Do not give the dog any compressions if there is a pulse, no matter how faint.
    (3) Check for a pulse and breathing every 2 minutes. If there is no pulse and breathing, continue for up to 10 minutes before giving up.

1

2

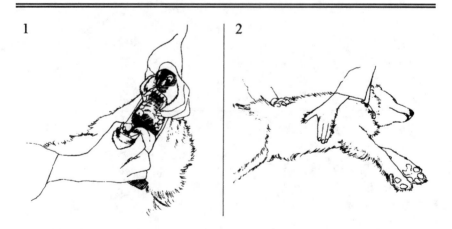

HOW TO MUZZLE A DOG

NOTE: Never apply a muzzle if the dog has difficulty breathing or is vomiting. Never muzzle a dog that has a flat face or small nostrils.

I. First-Aid Materials

A. A commercial muzzle (highly preferable to homemade), or

B. Materials to make a homemade muzzle:
    (1) 1 strip of gauze (3 feet long for a little dog or up to 6 feet long for a big dog)
    (2) Scissors

II. Making a Homemade Muzzle

A. Double the gauze strip and then tie a loose loop with the material. See the illustration below.

B. Approach the dog from the rear and slip this loop quickly over the dog's nose, guiding it back toward the corners of the mouth. Make the loop snug, but do not pinch the dog.

C. With the ends of the gauze strips, wrap the gauze around to the bottom of the dog's mouth, and then tie it behind the dog's ears.

III. Using a Muzzle

A. Approach the dog from behind, and apply the muzzle quickly.

B. It is helpful to have someone hold the dog's front feet down so that the pet won't pull off the muzzle.

C. Be prepared to remove the muzzle promptly if the dog has difficulty breathing or if there is any indication that the dog might vomit.

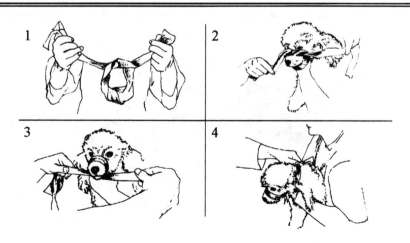

ELIZABETHAN COLLAR

An Elizabethan collar is a cone-shaped device that fits around the dog's neck. It is used to prevent a dog from instinctively licking or chewing an external injury. Elizabethan collars are available commercially, or you can follow the directions below to make one.

I. Materials
A. Medium-weight cardboard
B. Tape
C. Scissors

II. Technique Instructions
A. To construct a homemade Elizabethan collar:
  (1) Draw a circle on the cardboard (8 inches in diameter for a small dog with a small nose, up to 20 inches in diameter for a large dog with a long nose).
  (2) Cut out this circle.
  (3) Cut a circular hole the size of the dog's neck out of the center of the larger circle.
  (4) Make one cut from the outside diameter to the inside hole.
  (5) Slip the cardboard cut-out over the pet's head and secure the edges with tape to form a cone-like shape.
B. Fasten the collar securely, but make sure that it does not impede the dog's breathing. It should be loose enough for you to slip two fingers under the collar. It should be long enough to keep the pet from licking and chewing. It may take the dog some time to get used to the collar while walking, eating, and drinking.
C. Make sure the dog will eat and drink while wearing its collar.

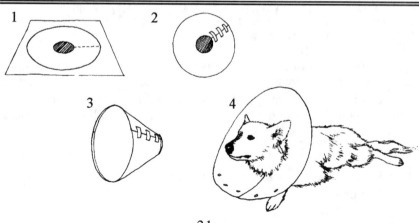

HELP FOR THE PROBLEM

ABRASIONS

I. Symptoms (some or all may be present)
A. Red skin
B. Missing hair
C. Painful area

II. First-Aid Materials
A. Contact-lens saline solution or water
B. Antibacterial soap
C. Clippers or scissors
D. Antibiotic ointment (e.g., Polysporin®)
E. Wrap material and/or Elizabethan collar

III. First Aid
A. Clip hair away from abrasion.
B. Cleanse the abrasion using soap and saline solution or water.
C. Apply antibiotic ointment to the abrasion.
D. If necessary, apply a wrap over the abrasion and/or use an Elizabethan collar to keep the dog from licking, scratching or chewing the area. See page 16 on Wrapping a Wound and page 21 on how to make an Elizabethan collar.
E. Seek veterinary help if the dog's discomfort persists.

ACETAMINOPHEN (TYLENOL®) INGESTION

In certain instances, veterinarians will prescribe acetaminophen to dogs, but accidental ingestion can be hazardous. No medications of any kind should be given to a dog without instructions from a veterinarian. Because dogs are curious by nature, all drugs should be kept out of your dog's reach to prevent accidental ingestion.

I. Symptoms (some or all may be present)
A. Listlessness

B. Difficult breathing
C. Vomiting and/or diarrhea
D. Dark-colored urine

II. First-Aid Materials
A. Hydrogen peroxide
B. Eyedropper or dosage syringe

III. First Aid
A. If the dog is conscious, induce vomiting immediately by feeding the pet 1 teaspoon of hydrogen peroxide (mixed with 1 teaspoon milk if available). For large dogs, over 60 pounds, double the dosage. If the dog will not drink the mixture or if there is no milk available, then force-feed the dog the hydrogen peroxide using an eyedropper. If vomiting does not occur within 10 minutes, repeat the procedure up to two times.
B. Contact a veterinarian for further treatment regardless of whether you are successful at inducing your dog to vomit.

ALLERGIES

In people, allergies often cause sneezing, runny eyes, and wheezing, whereas in dogs allergies usually cause itching and rashes. Although most skin irritations are not life-threatening emergencies, the degree of discomfort for the dog may be great. This section applies to both skin emergencies and minor skin irritations.

I. Symptoms (some or all may be present)
A. Red skin
B. Excess shedding
C. Missing hair
D. Painful area
E. Dog scratching itself

II. First-Aid Materials
A. Moisturizing shampoo
B. Elizabethan collar
C. Benadryl® or diphenhydramine elixir (12.5 mg per 5 ml liquid)

III. First Aid
A. Shampooing the pet will likely provide temporary relief from its symptoms. Use a shampoo for dogs (moisturizing shampoo is

best). While restraining the dog, lather the pet and let stand for 15-20 minutes. Rinse well with lukewarm tap water. Let the coat dry naturally. Consult your veterinarian for the proper type of shampoo and for specific instructions. A cold compress can be used over the most uncomfortable areas for 10 minutes every 2 hours.

B. If the dog is biting itself, you may need to apply an Elizabethan collar to prevent more damage to the skin. See page 21 on how to make and use an Elizabethan collar.

C. If you are unable to reach a veterinarian, give the dog Benadryl® or diphenhydramine elixir (12.5 mg per 5 ml liquid) as follows:
  (1) 1/4 teaspoon for dogs weighing less than five pounds.
  (2) 1/2 teaspoon for dogs weighing 5 to 10 pounds.
  (3) 1 to 1.5 teaspoons for dogs weighing 10 to 15 pounds.
  (4) 1.5 to 2 teaspoons for dogs weighing 15 to 25 pounds.
  (5) 2 to 3 teaspoons for dogs weighing 25 to 40 pounds.
  (6) 3 to 5 teaspoons for dogs weighing more than 40 pounds.

D. Seek veterinary help as soon as possible to give more permanent relief from the allergy.

ANAL GLAND/SAC ABSCESS

Anal glands/sacs are located along the side of the rectum at the 4 o'clock and 8 o'clock positions. They normally fill with a foul-smelling secretion that is discharged from the glands through small ducts during bowel movements. On occasion, these glands become infected or the ducts become plugged, and the secretion builds. The pressure in the glands becomes so great that the gland and the skin over the area break open and blood, pus and foul discharge may spill out.

I. Symptoms (some or all may be present)
A. Scooting butt on floor
B. Swelling around rectum
C. Open wound near rectum
D. Blood, pus or foul discharge under the tail
E. Difficulty sitting
F. Licking the rectum

II. First-Aid Materials
A. Muzzle

B. Pet shampoo or moisturizing shampoo

C. Antibiotic ointment (e.g., Polysporin®)

III. First Aid

A. You may wish to use a muzzle to prevent being bitten when you treat your dog. However, use a muzzle only if the dog is not having difficulty breathing and has not been vomiting. If at any time the dog has difficulty breathing, remove the muzzle. Also, do not use a muzzle if your dog has a flat face (e.g., a pug, boxer, English bulldog, etc.).

B. Fill a bathtub with warm water, and have the dog sit in the tub for 10 to 20 minutes.

C. If the dog is not in too much pain, cleanse the area under its tail with shampoo, and then rinse well. Dry the dog with a towel.

D. Apply antibiotic ointment (e.g., Polysporin®) to any open wounds.

E. If necessary, apply an Elizabethan collar to prevent the dog from licking its rectum.

F. Contact a veterinarian for additional care.

ANEMIA

Anemia has many causes, but regardless of the origin of the anemia, the result is an inability of the blood to carry oxygen. Causes of anemia in dogs include flea bites, internal or external bleeding, poisonings, autoimmune diseases, cancers and nutritional deficiencies. It is important that the dog receive proper diagnosis of the condition from a veterinarian so that appropriate treatment can be administered.

I. Symptoms (some or all may be present)

A. Listlessness and depression

B. Pale or white gums

C. Loss of appetite

D. Labored breathing

E. Collapse

II. First Aid

A. The dog should see a veterinarian for proper diagnosis as soon as possible.

B. Minimize stress during handling and transportation.

C. Feed the dog a balanced dog-diet with an appropriate vitamin

supplement prescribed by your veterinarian. Hand feed if
necessary.

ANTIFREEZE TOXICITY

Antifreeze (ethylene glycol) is a common poison to pets for
three reasons: (1) it is a commonly used product, (2) it is often
improperly discarded, and (3) it is sweet to the taste.

Antifreeze contains ethylene glycol which, when metabolized,
causes kidney damage that is usually fatal. Even a small amount will
cause severe illness or death. Because the toxin is rapidly absorbed,
symptoms may appear as early as one hour after ingestion.
Symptoms are vague and mimic those of many other conditions and
diseases.

I. **Symptoms (some or all may be present)**
A. Increased thirst
B. Vomiting and diarrhea
C. Depression
D. Loss of coordination
E. Kidney failure (sometimes preceded by apparent improvement in
the dog's condition)

II. **First-Aid Materials**
A. Hydrogen peroxide
B. Liquor (e.g., vodka, whiskey, gin, rum)
C. Eyedropper or dosage syringe

III. **First Aid**
A. If an exposure is suspected, induce vomiting by feeding the dog
1 teaspoon of hydrogen peroxide (mixed with 1 teaspoon milk if
available). If the dog will not drink the mixture or if there is no
milk available, then force-feed the dog the hydrogen peroxide
using an eyedropper or dosage syringe. If vomiting does not
occur within 10 minutes, repeat the procedure up to two times.
B. Get immediate veterinary help.
C. If a veterinarian cannot be found, then when vomiting ceases or
if vomiting cannot be induced, feed the dog, using an
eyedropper or dosage syringe, 1 to 2 tablespoons (or 15cc to 30
cc) of liquor (e.g., vodka, whiskey, gin, rum) mixed with an equal
amount of milk. (If milk is not available, then use water.) Wait

26

10 minutes, and if there are no signs of depression or intoxication, administer another 1 tablespoon (15 cc) of liquor mixed with 1 tablespoon (15 cc) of milk or water. (The ethanol in liquor competes with the ethylene glycol metabolism, and can thereby reduce the damage that ethylene glycol causes to the kidneys. It also promotes increased urination to allow faster excretion of the poison.)

D. Seek veterinary attention for further treatment.

BACK AND NECK INJURY

Back and neck injury may result from muscle strain, trauma or a variety of other situations. The injury may even be a herniated disc (see pages 81-82), embolism, or possibly a tumor near the spine.

I. Symptoms (some or all may be present)
A. Restricted or painful movement
B. Difficulty lifting head
C. Lameness
D. Walking hunched-over
E. Depression and loss of appetite
F. Paralysis (if the spinal cord is affected)

II. First-Aid Materials
A. Pet carrier (if you have a small dog)
B. Towels
C. Blanket
D. 2-liter soda bottle filled with warm water
E. Muzzle
F. Plywood board cut to fit your dog and your car

III. First Aid
A. Seek veterinary advice immediately. Back and neck injuries require professional attention.
B. Restrict the dog's activity. Minimize handling and movement of the dog.
C. If you need to transport your dog, plan the transport carefully to minimize movement of the dog. See *Transporting a Dog with Fractures or Back Injuries* on pages 13-14.
D. If the injury appears to be serious, treat for shock: see page 79.

BEE STINGS

When a dog is stung, it is usually stung on an exposed area, such as the nose or mouth. Fortunately, severe allergic reactions are less common in dogs than in humans. However, bee stings are painful and should be treated, especially if there is any indication of an allergic reaction.

I.   Symptoms (some or all may be present)
A.   Dog scratching and rubbing the area of the sting
B.   Swelling
C.   Enlargement of the lips or nose (because most stings are to the face and mouth)
D.   Difficulty breathing (though less common in dogs than in people)

II.   First-Aid Materials
A.   Ice
B.   Towel
C.   Benadryl® or diphenhydramine elixir (12.5 mg per 5 ml liquid)

III.   First Aid
A.   Apply ice wrapped in a towel over the swollen, painful areas.
B.   Seek veterinary attention for medication.
C.   If you are unable to reach a veterinarian, give the dog Benadryl® or diphenhydramine elixir (12.5 mg per 5 ml liquid) as follows:
   (1)   1/4 teaspoon for dogs weighing less than five pounds.
   (2)   1/2 teaspoon for dogs weighing 5 to 10 pounds.
   (3)   1 to 1.5 teaspoons for dogs weighing 10 to 15 pounds.
   (4)   1.5 to 2 teaspoons for dogs weighing 15 to 25 pounds.
   (5)   2 to 3 teaspoons for dogs weighing 25 to 40 pounds.
   (6)   3 to 5 teaspoons for dogs weighing more than 40 pounds.
D.   If there is no improvement within 1 hour after administering medication, or if the condition worsens, seek veterinary assistance.

BITE WOUNDS

Dogs commonly fight among themselves and with other animals. Bite wounds are often more serious than they may at first appear because the damage on the surface of the skin is usually less

severe than the injury to underlying tissue. Bite wounds often become infected, resulting in a local accumulation of pus (a bite wound abscess) inside the wound site. Often the abscess will break open and drain, which is part of the healing process. See page 31.

I. **Symptoms (some or all may be present)**
A. Punctured, torn or lacerated skin with or without bleeding
B. Swelling
C. Painful area
D. Depression, loss of appetite or other signs of illness

II. **First-Aid Materials**
A. Contact-lens saline solution or water
B. Antibacterial soap
C. Clippers or scissors
D. Antibiotic ointment (e.g., Polysporin®)
E. Wrap material and/or Elizabethan collar

III. **First Aid**
A. Clip hair away from wound.
B. Cleanse the wound using soap and saline solution or water.
C. Apply antibiotic ointment to the wound.
D. If necessary, apply a wrap over the wound and/or use an Elizabethan collar to keep the dog from licking, scratching or chewing the area. See page 16 on Wrapping a Wound and page 21 on how to make an Elizabethan collar.
E. Seek veterinary help for antibiotic therapy.

BLEEDING

External bleeding may result from an abrasion or laceration, trauma (e.g., gunshot wound, hit by car), bite wound abscess or compound fracture. Internal bleeding may result from trauma that does not cause a break in the skin, injury to a large muscle mass, a bone fracture, a tumor, toxicity from rat poisoning, an immune disorder, or injury of an internal organ. Whenever significant bleeding occurs, immediate action is required to prevent shock.

I. **Symptoms (some or all may be present)**
A. Blood coming from a wound

B. Blood accumulating under the skin, looking like a bruise
C. Blood in the dog's urine, feces or vomitus
D. Weakness
E. Pale gums
F. Labored breathing
G. Distended (enlarged) abdomen

II. First-Aid Materials
A. Clean towel
B. Gauze sponges
C. Nonstick adhesive tape
D. Nonstick bandages
E. Gauze wrap

III. First Aid
A. For internal bleeding:
    (1) Seek veterinary assistance immediately. Internal bleeding is an emergency requiring immediate professional assistance.
    (2) Avoid anything that may stress the pet. The least bit of stress may precipitate a crisis when the pet cannot breathe.
    (3) Do not monitor vital signs.
    (4) Plan the handling of the dog to minimize excitement. Never hold the dog tightly.
B. For external bleeding:
    (1) Locate the source of bleeding.
    (2) Using a clean towel or gauze sponges, apply direct pressure to the wound for 5-10 minutes.
    (3) If the bleeding does not stop, apply a wrap as follows:
        a) Press nonstick bandage to wound.
        b) Secure nonstick bandage to wound by wrapping gauze around the leg or body. The gauze should be snug but not tight. The wrap tightness should not restrict the dog's circulation or breathing.
        c) Secure the gauze by applying adhesive tape to the wrap.
        d) Monitor the pet for any evidence of swelling to the limb below the wrap. If swelling occurs, then the wrap is too tight and should be removed immediately. Also, if the dog's breathing is hindered, you should remove the wrap.
        e) Do not attempt to apply a tourniquet, even if the injury is a severed tail.
    (4) If the bleeding was difficult to stop, do not attempt to clean

the wound or apply antibiotic ointment; the clot may be disrupted and severe hemorrhage may resume.

    (5) For future reference, note the amount of blood loss. If the injury seems severe, treat the dog for shock as follows:

        a) Keep the dog warm by placing a 2-liter soda bottle filled with warm water (not hot water) against the dog. Cover the dog with a towel or blanket.

        b) Monitor the dog's vital signs (temperature, pulse and respirations) every 15 minutes, and record the information. Try to keep the dog's temperature within the range of 101-102.5 degrees Fahrenheit. If the dog's temperature rises above 102.5 degrees Fahrenheit, remove the warm soda bottle. If the dog's temperature falls below 101 degrees, place an additional warm-water soda bottle against the dog, but make sure the water is not hot and make sure the bottle is against the dog and not on top of or underneath the dog.

    (6) Call your veterinarian immediately. For best healing, lacerations should be repaired as soon as possible (ideally within one hour of the injury). As time elapses, the wound becomes contaminated and may not be able to be closed.

C. For bleeding from the mouth:

    (1) Do not muzzle the dog.

    (2) If there is bleeding from the mouth but no injury to the mouth, follow procedures for internal bleeding, page 30.

    (3) If the outside of the mouth is bleeding, follow the instructions for external bleeding on pages 30-31.

    (4) If the dog has lost one or more teeth:

        (a) If you can find the teeth, pick them up by the crown (i.e., NOT by the roots) and place them in a cup of milk. The milk will preserve the teeth short-term and may enable your veterinarian to save them.

        (b) Seek veterinary assistance immediately.

D. For bite wound abscess bleeding, apply warm compresses to the area to promote drainage. The abscess may rupture and spill out blood and pus, but this will actually make the pet feel better.

BLOAT AND TWISTED STOMACH

When a dog's stomach becomes distended by gas (a condition called "bloat") or when the stomach actually twists and cuts off the blood supply to the stomach (called "twisted stomach," "gastric volvulus" or "gastric torsion"), the result is extreme pain. If the dog does not receive immediate veterinary care, the condition is usually fatal.

Bloat and twisted stomach are conditions of unknown origin. Deep-chested dogs (e.g., Great Danes, St. Bernards, Weimaraners, Dobermans, golden retrievers, Irish setters, German shepherds, etc.) are more predisposed than others to these conditions. Some veterinarians recommend that deep-chested dogs not be exercised shortly after they have eaten as a precautionary measure for avoiding bloat and twisted stomach.

I. **Symptoms (some or all may be present)**
A. Belching
B. Increased gas noises from abdomen
C. Dry heaves or retching (i.e., unable to vomit)
D. Distended abdomen (usually, but not always)
E. Restlessness or pacing
F. Crying
G. Anxiety followed by depression
H. Collapse

II. **First-Aid Materials**
A. 2-liter soda bottle
B. Blanket or towels
C. Thermometer

III. **First Aid**
A. Contact a veterinarian immediately. The conditions are life-threatening and may require immediate surgery.
B. Keep the dog warm by placing a 2-liter soda bottle filled with warm water (not hot water) against the dog. See illustrations on page 80. Cover the dog with a towel or blanket.
C. Monitor the dog's vital signs (temperature, pulse and respirations) every 15 minutes and record the information. Try to keep the dog's temperature within the range of 101-102.5 degrees Fahrenheit. If the dog's temperature rises above 102.5 degrees Fahrenheit, remove the warm soda bottle. If the dog's

temperature falls below 101 degrees, place an additional warm water soda bottle against the dog, but make sure the water is not hot and make sure the bottle is against the dog and not on top of or underneath the dog. See illustrations on page 80.

BREATHING DIFFICULTIES

I. Problems/Conditions with that Symptom
A. Heart disease/lung disease
B. Heat stroke
C. Internal bleeding
D. Shock/trauma
E. Anemia
F. Open chest wound or fractured ribs
G. Poisoning
H. Asthma
I. Obstruction of the airway
J. Bee and scorpion stings
K. Smoke inhalation
L. Most other medical emergencies

II. First-Aid Materials
A. Two 2-liter soda bottles
B. Blanket

III. First Aid
A. Avoid anything that may stress the pet. The least bit of stress may precipitate a crisis when the pet cannot breathe.
B. Do not monitor vital signs.
C. Plan the handling of the dog to minimize excitement. Never hold tightly.
D. Never lay the dog on its back or side because this will compromise oxygen exchange by putting extra pressure on the chest.
E. Seal any open chest wound with plastic wrap, and then cover with a bandage. Make sure the bandage does not restrict breathing.
F. Contact a veterinarian immediately.

BROKEN TEETH

Broken teeth can sometimes be saved if you react quickly and appropriately. The condition can be extremely painful and should be treated by a veterinarian right away.

I. **Symptoms**
A. Pawing at mouth
B. Signs of pain and distress
C. Missing tooth/teeth

II. **First-Aid Materials**
A. Milk

III. **First Aid**
A. If the dog has lost one or more permanent teeth, and you can find the missing tooth/teeth, pick them up by the crown (i.e., NOT by the roots) and place them in a cup of milk. The milk will preserve the teeth short-term and may enable your veterinarian to save them.
B. Seek veterinary assistance immediately.

BUMPS/LUMPS/HIVES

I. **Problems/Conditions with that Symptom**
A. Allergy/hives
B. Insect bites and stings
C. Drug reactions
D. Bite wounds
E. Tumor, cyst or swollen lymph nodes

II. **First-Aid Materials**
A. Towel(s)
B. Ice
C. Benadryl® or diphenhydramine elixir (12.5 mg per 5 ml liquid)

III. **First Aid**
A. If the dog is uncomfortable, place a towel moistened with cold water, or ice wrapped in a towel, over the irritated areas. This is especially soothing for hives and insect bites and stings.
B. If you are unable to reach a veterinarian, and you suspect that

the bumps/lumps are hives, allergies, insect bites or insect stings, you may give the dog Benadryl® or diphenhydramine elixir (12.5 mg per 5 ml liquid) as follows:

    (1) 1/4 teaspoon for dogs weighing less than five pounds.

    (2) 1/2 teaspoon for dogs weighing 5 to 10 pounds.

    (3) 1 to 1.5 teaspoons for dogs weighing 10 to 15 pounds.

    (4) 1.5 to 2 teaspoons for dogs weighing 15 to 25 pounds.

    (5) 2 to 3 teaspoons for dogs weighing 25 to 40 pounds.

    (6) 3 to 5 teaspoons for dogs weighing more than 40 pounds.

C.   Seek veterinary help.

BURNS

Many burns are not evident when they occur because the fur often conceals the injury to the skin. Burns can result from a variety of sources including chemicals, plants, heat, electricity and hot water. Burns should always be treated as soon as possible.

I.   Symptoms (some or all may be present)

A.   If the fur is still present, the area of the burn may feel like a thickened area under the hair coat.

B.   Burned area may feel hardened and may or may not be painful.

C.   The pet may lick or scratch at the affected area.

D.   If the burn is not recognized early, the fur and skin may start to peel away from the dog's body, leaving a deep, weeping sore.

E.   Signs of secondary complications include weakness (from dehydration), infections and depression.

II.   First-Aid Materials

A.   Pet shampoo

B.   Contact-lens saline solution

C.   Antibiotic ointment (e.g., Polysporin®)

D.   Baking soda

E.   Vinegar

III. First Aid

A.   **If the burn was caused by unknown chemicals,**

    (1) Bathe the dog immediately to remove any remaining chemicals. Use copious amounts of water. If available, use a pet shampoo (lather, let stand for 10 minutes, rinse).

    (2) Rinse the burned area in saline, and then cover the wound

with antibiotic ointment. If the dog licks or scratches the area, cover the burn with a wrap (as shown on page 16).

B. **If the burn was caused by an acid,**
   (1) Rinse the area with copious amounts of water.
   (2) Apply a paste of 1 part baking soda to 2 parts water to the affected areas.

C. **If the burn was caused by an alkali,**
   (1) Rinse the area with copious amounts of water.
   (2) Apply a solution of 1 part vinegar to 4 parts water.

D. **If the burn was caused by electricity,**
   (1) Cover the wound with antibiotic ointment. If the dog licks or scratches the area, cover the burn with a wrap. (See Wrapping a Wound on page 16.)
   (2) Seek veterinary assistance immediately because electric shock can cause dangerous arrhythmias (i.e., heart damage).

E. Because burns can have serious side effects, such as dehydration and secondary infections, seek prompt veterinary care.

CHOCOLATE TOXICITY - See page 96.

CHOKING

It is not common for a dog to choke on its food. When choking does occur in dogs, it is frequently the result of something being lodged in the dog's mouth, such as a toy, bone or rawhide. If you give your dog rawhide, make sure that the rawhide is too large for the pet to swallow, and when it becomes smaller from the dog's chewing, discard it promptly. See the section on Prevention starting on page 6 of this book for some precautions for avoiding choking.

I. **Symptoms (some or all may be present)**
A. Drooling
B. Pawing at mouth
C. Collapse
D. Labored breathing
E. Anxious behavior

II. **Problems/Conditions with that Symptom**
A. Foreign body
B. Aspiration of fluid
C. Nausea

III. First-Aid Materials
A. 1-inch roll of tape
B. Pencil with eraser

IV. First Aid
A. Open the dog's mouth to see whether a foreign object is lodged in the dog's mouth or throat, but take care to prevent being bitten. If necessary, use a small roll of first-aid tape as a wedge to keep the dog's mouth open to allow better access and to protect you from the dog's teeth. (See illustration below.)
B. If the dog's airway is not blocked, wait for veterinary assistance before attempting to remove any object; your efforts could do more harm than good. If the airway is blocked, use the eraser end of a pencil to try gently to dislodge the object.
C. If fluid is causing the choking, try wiping the fluid from the mouth using a tissue. You may need to hold the dog with its head lower than its chest for 5 to 10 seconds in order for the fluid to drain. Repeat this process no more than five times.
D. If the pet becomes unconscious:
   (1) Observe for breathing; see if the dog's chest rises and falls.
   (2) **If the dog is breathing**, proceed to Step F; do not use CPR.
E. **If the dog is not breathing**, proceed with CPR as directed on pages 18-19.
F. Sedation may be necessary to remove a foreign object; if your attempt at home is unsuccessful, seek immediate veterinary care.
G. Regardless of whether the object has been removed, have your dog checked by a veterinarian as soon as possible for lacerations in the mouth and throat.

37

COLITIS

Colitis is inflammation of the colon. It has many different causes including allergic reactions, dietary indiscretions, foreign bodies, parasitic infestations and cancers. Even though not all causes of colitis are serious, the amount of discomfort the dog feels warrants the classification of colitis as an emergency.

I. **Symptoms (some or all may be present)**
A. Blood or mucous in the stool
B. Soft stools – If bowel movements cannot be observed, check under the dog's tail for stool pasted to the fur.
C. Foreign material (e.g., string, grass, panty hose, socks, etc.) protruding from the rectum – **Do not pull on these objects because they could tear or cut the bowels.**
D. Straining – (NOTE: straining may indicate a life-threatening urinary blockage. Watch to make sure the dog urinates.)

II. **First Aid**
A. If there is no foreign object protruding from the rectum and there are no signs of illness other than colitis, withhold food for 4 hours. (This time reference is for a normal, otherwise healthy, adult dog. Puppies and old dogs should not be restricted from food for more than a couple of hours.) DO NOT withhold water unless your dog is vomiting. If there are other symptoms of illness, such as vomiting, lack of appetite or listlessness, contact a veterinarian immediately. If your dog has no symptoms of other illness but is not more comfortable within 4 hours, contact a veterinarian. Many times colitis requires treatment with antibiotics or anti-inflammatory drugs.
B. If any foreign object (e.g., grass, string, cloth, etc.) is protruding from the rectum, do not pull on the object; it could lacerate the bowels. If the object is protruding more than four inches, cut the object with a scissors (to within four inches of the rectum) taking care not to cut the dog. Contact a veterinarian immediately.
C. Add 1-2 teaspoons of bran flakes and 3 tablespoons of plain yogurt to your dog's meals to increase the fiber in your pet's diet and replace normal digestive flora, or obtain a prescription food from your veterinarian.
D. To aid your dog's digestion, feed your dog more frequently but in smaller portions.

COLLAPSE

I. Problems/Conditions with that Symptom
A. Anemia
B. Bloat (gastric dilation volvulus) or twisted stomach
C. Diabetes
D. Heart disease
E. Heat stroke
F. Hypoadrenocorticism (Addison's disease)
G. Hypoglycemia (low blood sugar)
H. Hypothermia
I. Infections
J. Internal bleeding
K. Lung disease
L. Poisonings
M. Seizures
N. Shock/trauma
O. Urinary blockage

II. First-Aid Materials
A. Two 2-liter soda bottles
B. Blanket
C. Corn syrup (e.g., Karo® syrup), if collapse is from diabetes

III. First Aid
A. If the dog is diabetic, the cause of the collapse could be insulin shock. If so, rub the dog's gums with corn syrup.
B. If the pet is unconscious, check for breathing by watching the dog's chest rise and fall.
C. **If the dog is breathing,** proceed to Step E. Do not use CPR.
D. **If the dog is not breathing,** do CPR as directed on pages 18-19.
E. If the dog is conscious, proceed as follows:
    (1) Keep the pet calm, and avoid unnecessary stress. Do not monitor vital signs, and do not use excessive restraint or cause excessive movement. Plan the handling of the dog to minimize stress. Never hold the dog tightly.
    (2) Lay the dog upright (i.e., belly down). (If the dog is on its back or side, there is extra pressure on the chest making it harder for the pet to breathe.)
F. Seek immediate veterinary care.

CONSTIPATION

Dogs rarely become constipated, but when they do, causes include dehydration, perianal hernias, prostatic enlargement and foreign bodies in the digestive tract. Note, however, that a dog that strains to have a bowel movement is not necessarily constipated. (See Colitis on page 38, Straining on pages 84-85, and Urinary Tract Irritations on pages 88-89.)

I. **Symptoms (some or all may be present)**
A. Lack of bowel movement within 48 hours
B. Straining to go to the bathroom
C. Loss of appetite

II. **First-Aid Materials**
A. Bran flakes
B. Mineral oil

III. **First Aid**
A. If the dog is uncomfortable or if more than 2 days have passed since a bowel movement, contact your veterinarian.
B. Most dogs do not tolerate home enemas. An enema should be performed by a professional because a dog can be injured easily if it struggles during the process.
C. Feed the dog 2 tablespoons of bran flakes with each meal.
D. Encourage the dog to drink water.
E. Mix 1/4 teaspoon mineral oil into the dog's food to soften the dog's stools.

COUGHING

I. **Problems/Conditions with that Symptom**
A. Heart disease
B. Lung disease
C. Infections
D. Bronchitis or tonsillitis
E. Asthma
F. Smoke inhalation
G. Obstruction from a foreign object

II. First-Aid Materials
A. Water

III. First Aid
A. If the cause of the cough is unknown, offer water to the pet.
B. If the cough persists, see a veterinarian as soon as possible. Note whether the cough is dry or productive so that your veterinarian can better advise you regarding additional treatment.
C. If the dog's breathing becomes labored, refer to Breathing Difficulties on page 33.

DELIVERIES

While most deliveries are routine and can be accomplished without any human intervention, sometimes complications occur. This chapter will assist you in identifying delivery problems.

I. Preparation for Delivery
A. Gather the following materials: a large box, clean towels, thread, warm water bottles and emergency formula. (See page 76 for a homemade emergency formula.)
B. Make sure the dog has a clean nesting area for the delivery. A large box 2 to 3 feet square and 6 inches high lined with a clean towel is ideal for a small dog, while a corner of a room or closet with a large clean towel or sheet is appropriate for large dogs.
C. Handle the dog as little as possible.

II. Helping with a Delivery
A. Try not to disturb the dog during the delivery process, but try to monitor her progress by quietly observing her actions.
B. If a puppy is being passed and is having difficulty clearing the vulva, you may exert gentle downward pressure on the puppy to help it pass.
C. If the mother is not cleaning the puppies after delivery, use a towel and remove any fluid from the nose and mouth. Then dry the puppy using a gentle rubbing action.
D. Occasionally the umbilical cord will not separate from the mother and puppy. If this occurs, take a thread and tie a knot 1/2 inch from the puppy's belly, and then cut the cord with scissors between the knot and the mother dog. This will prevent bleeding from tearing the cord.

E. If a puppy is not breathing, continue to stimulate the puppy by rubbing it vigorously; at the same time blow into its nose every 5 seconds to give it air. Try this for at least 5 minutes.

F. The puppies should be placed at the mother's breast to ensure they nurse. Keep track of any puppies that do not nurse; they may need to be hand fed.

G. If the puppies cry, they may be hungry, cold, or sick. Contact your veterinarian if the crying persists.

III. Signs of a Difficult Delivery

A. If more than 20 minutes pass between puppies and the mother is having strong contractions, call your veterinarian.

B. If labor continues for more than an hour without the birth of a puppy, call your veterinarian.

C. When there is a weak contraction for a period of 1 hour between bouts of active labor, but no puppy is delivered, call your veterinarian.

D. If you observe any evidence of unusual pain during the delivery, such as crying or excessive biting or licking of the hind quarters, call your veterinarian.

E. If the pregnancy exceeds 70 days, call your veterinarian.

F. If there is an unusual discharge coming from the vulva under the tail, call your veterinarian. Normal discharge is green (not black, bloody, cloudy, or foul-smelling).

G. If there is normal greenish discharge without the birth of a puppy, call your veterinarian.

H. If the dog shows symptoms of illness, like depression, vomiting, diarrhea or weakness, call your veterinarian.

DIARRHEA

The goal in helping a dog with diarrhea is to comfort the pet and lessen the symptoms until the cause can be determined. There are many causes of diarrhea, including infections, dietary changes, foreign bodies, parasites and poisons.

I. Symptoms (some or all may be present)

A. Soft to watery stools

B. Loss of appetite

C. Painful abdomen

II. Problems/Conditions with that Symptom
A. Heat stroke
B. Shock/trauma
C. Infections
D. Poisonings
E. Parasites
F. Cancer
G. Dietary changes or indiscretions
H. Foreign objects

III. First-Aid Materials
A. Plain yogurt
B. Boiled hamburger and plain cooked rice

IV. First Aid
A. If there is no vomiting, feed your dog 2 to 3 tablespoons of plain yogurt. DO NOT administer human medications for diarrhea; they often contain salicylates that can react with other medicines and complicate a digestive upset.
B. Repeat Step A every 4 to 6 hours for adult dogs and every 2 to 4 hours for puppies less than 14 weeks old.
C. Withhold food for 2-4 hours if diarrhea is present and if there is no other symptom of illness. Withhold both food and water if the dog is also vomiting, but do not withhold water for more than 2 hours. Do not withhold water if the dog is not vomiting. The time period for withholding food should be based on whether your pet is a normal, healthy adult versus a puppy, an elderly dog or a dog with any special or compromising conditions. If your dog has diabetes or any other illness or medical condition, consult your veterinarian first before withholding food and water.
D. When you do resume feeding your dog, the best home remedy for diarrhea is to prepare a 50/50 mixture of boiled hamburger (drain off the water and fat) and plain cooked rice. Appropriate feedings are as follows:
(1) 1/4 cup of the mixture 4 times per day for small dogs,
(2) 1/2 cup of the mixture 4 times per day for medium dogs,
(3) 3/4 cup of the mixture 4 times per day for large dogs.
Your veterinarian may wish to adjust the servings or may recommend a prescription diet instead.
E. Note the frequency and substance of the diarrhea.
F. If symptoms persist for more than 4 hours, or if they worsen or return, contact the pet's doctor immediately.

G. If a dog has other signs along with the diarrhea (e.g., vomiting, loss of coordination, fatigue, etc.) contact a veterinarian.
H. Because some infections can be transmitted to people, wash your hands after handling the dog or cleaning up accidents.

V. Veterinary Care
A. Your veterinarian may request a stool sample for examination under the microscope (to check for intestinal parasites).
B. Proper diagnosis and medication from your veterinarian can prevent serious side effects from the diarrhea.

DISEMBOWELMENT

I. Problems/Conditions with that Symptom
A. Severe trauma
B. Postoperative complications

II. First-Aid Materials
A. Towel and/or gauze sponges
B. Contact-lens saline solution

III. First Aid
A. Contact a veterinarian immediately.
B. Soak a towel or gauze sponges with saline solution, and apply it to the area of protrusion to keep the organs from becoming dehydrated.
C. Keep the organs covered with the wet towel and/or wet sponges to keep the dog from mutilating itself. Dogs will often chew on exposed bowels.
D. Use an Elizabethan collar if the dog is attempting to chew or scratch the injury. See page 21.

DROOLING

I. Problems/Conditions with that Symptom
A. Nausea
B. Gum irritation
C. Diseased teeth

D. Foreign body in mouth
E. Chemical or plant exposure/poisoning
F. Contagious disease (e.g., rabies)

II. First-Aid Materials
A. Pet shampoo

III. First Aid
A. Determine whether your pet may have been exposed to a poison. If so, try to determine the type of poison. Then use the index of this book to find emergency treatment for ingestion of poison in general or, ideally, for ingestion of the particular substance.
B. If there was a flea chemical recently applied to the dog (i.e., that same day), bathe the dog with pet shampoo that does not contain flea chemicals to remove excess chemicals from the coat. Most drooling should stop within 30 minutes.
C. If poisoning or chemicals do not appear to be the cause, check the dog's mouth for diseased teeth, irritated gums and foreign objects by opening the dog's jaws and lifting the dog's lips. (See illustration on page 19.) Do not attempt to remove any object that is wedged in the dog's mouth unless the airway becomes completely blocked; your efforts could injure the dog's mouth or throat. Instead, seek veterinary assistance immediately.
D. If the cause is unknown and the drooling persists, withhold food and water temporarily and contact a veterinarian immediately.

DROWNING

Dogs that love to swim or ride in boats or live near any body of water, including flood plains, are at risk of drowning. While most dogs are natural swimmers, some are better than others, and waves, undertows or fast currents may be more than your dog can handle.

I. Symptoms (one or both may be present)
A. Witnessing the event
B. Finding the dog collapsed on a shoreline

II. First Aid
A. Hold the dog upside-down by its hind legs to allow the water and fluid to drain from its airway. Gently pounding the dog's chest may hasten fluid removal.

45

B. Check for breathing by watching the dog's chest rise and fall.
C. **If the dog is breathing**, proceed to Step E. Do not use CPR.
D. **If the dog is not breathing**, perform CPR as directed on page 18.
E. Seek veterinary help for treatment to remove residual fluid, treat for infection and monitor the dog's condition.

EXTERNAL PARASITES

External parasites include fleas, ticks and lice. These parasites not only cause blood loss (sometimes resulting in anemia) but may also transmit diseases. It is important to note that a severe flea infestation may be extremely difficult to treat effectively, both in terms of your pet and your home. Prevention (e.g., use of a flea-prevention product) and early treatment are critical in keeping the situation from developing into a major problem.

FLEAS – Whenever you are using flea products either as prevention or treatment, it is important to read all instructions thoroughly. Products that are used improperly or used in the wrong combination can be harmful to your dog. If your dog has an adverse reaction to any type of flea treatment, discontinue the treatment and contact a veterinarian immediately.

I. **Symptoms (some or all may be present)**
A. Fleas visible crawling through the dog's hair coat or jumping on or off of the dog – They are very small dark insects, so small they are difficult to see.
B. Flea droppings – Even if you cannot see the fleas, you may see flea droppings, which appear as black specks throughout the dog's hair coat. These black specks are actually the fleas' waste products that consist of the dog's blood.
C. Weakness from anemia (see page 25)
D. Weight loss
E. Scratching (though not all dogs with fleas will scratch)

II. **Pet Care**
A. Consult your veterinarian. A number of external parasite-control protocols can be prescribed.
B. All products used should be labeled for dogs. These products should be used only as directed.

C. If you cannot consult a veterinarian, bathe the pet in flea shampoo to remove the fleas and the flea droppings.
D. Treat the dog using a flea product approved for use on dogs. The flea product will kill residual fleas and keep other fleas off. Treat regularly as directed by your veterinarian.
E. Begin treatments as soon as you are aware of a flea problem. The longer you wait, the more difficult it will be to get rid of them.
F. If you witness any unusual reactions to any flea treatments (e.g., drooling lasting longer than 20 minutes, tremors, seizures, respiratory difficulty, etc.), discontinue the treatments immediately, and contact your veterinarian.

III. Environmental Treatment
A. Inside the house:
    (1) The dogs and the environment should be treated at the same time.
    (2) Vacuum the home thoroughly.
    (3) Discard vacuum cleaner bag.
    (4) Wash the dog's bedding regularly.
    (5) Using hand-held premises spray, treat all corners, baseboards, throw rugs, closets and cracks where foggers will not penetrate. Follow the instructions as directed on the product label.
    (6) Place foggers strategically through the house in each closed room. Foggers will not penetrate through doorways or down hallways. Follow the instructions on the label.
    (7) Repeat, if necessary, as directed by product label.
B. Outside the house treatment:
    (1) Treat the yard with a yard and kennel spray as directed on the product label.
    (2) Keep outside rest areas clean and dry.

LICE – These parasites not only cause blood loss, sometimes resulting in life-threatening anemia (see page 25), but may also transmit diseases. Lice in large numbers can drain enough blood to kill a dog.

I. General Information
A. Lice are slightly larger than fleas, and unlike fleas, their backs are flat.
B. The eggs or nits are seen as light specks along the hair shafts.

II. Pet Care
A. Bathe your dog in a flea and tick shampoo as directed.
B. Once the dog is dry, apply a flea and tick product approved for use on dogs.
C. Contact your family doctor and your veterinarian for details on transmission to people.

TICKS – Ticks transit diseases that can be harmful or fatal to dogs and people. When it comes to ticks, prevention is definitely the best medicine.

I. General Information
A. Ticks are eight-legged parasites. The tick's body is flat, hard, and shiny but becomes soft and enlarged after feeding on a dog.
B. Ticks may carry diseases such as Lyme disease, Rocky Mountain spotted fever, and tick paralysis.
C. Ticks embed their mouth parts only into the skin. A tick's head, therefore, cannot be left behind in the dog's skin (i.e., when you remove the tick), but it is possible for the area to become infected or irritated, mimicking the presence of something under the skin.

II. How to Remove a Tick
A. Apply a flea and tick product for dogs directly on the tick, and wait one minute. Then, using tweezers or wearing disposable gloves, apply constant pull while grasping the tick's body. The tick should release.
B. Do not try to burn the tick or apply any other type of chemical to the tick. If flea or tick spray is not available, simply pull with constant pressure until the tick releases.
C. Dispose of the tick carefully. Make sure it is dead by spraying it with tick spray, or dispose of it by flushing it down the toilet. Avoid touching the tick with your bare hands.
D. Apply antibiotic ointment where the tick was removed.
E. If any unusual symptoms develop after the removal of the tick, contact your veterinarian.

III. Prevention
A. Use a flea and tick product on a regular basis.
B. Examine your dog every time the pet comes into the house from outside, or at least once daily.

EYE EMERGENCIES

Examples of eye emergencies include corneal scratches, glaucoma, contusions, corneal ulcers, foreign debris in the eyes and popped-out (proptosed) eyes. A delay in treatment may result in permanent loss of vision.

I. **Symptoms (some or all may be present)**
A. Squinting
B. Excessive tearing (may be clear or cloudy)
C. Dog rubbing its eye(s) with its paw or rubbing its face on the ground
D. Enlarged eye(s)
E. Reddened white of the eye(s)
F. Protruding eye(s)

II. **First-Aid Materials**
A. Contact-lens saline solution
B. Gauze sponges

III. **First Aid**
A. If the irritation is minor, gently rinse the eye(s) with the contact-lens saline solution by applying several drops to the affected eye(s). This may dislodge any foreign debris causing the irritation. If the irritation is serious, contact professional help immediately. Never remove foreign debris that is penetrating the cornea because the eye might rupture.
B. If the symptoms persist, worsen or improve but then reappear, call the dog's veterinarian.
C. For a protruding eye, soak a gauze sponge with saline solution and apply to the eye, or apply several drops of saline directly onto the affected eye every five minutes. This will keep the eye from becoming dehydrated. DO NOT apply pressure to the eye to stop bleeding.
D. To keep the dog from further injuring the eye, apply an Elizabethan collar. (See page 21.)
E.. Never apply human medicine to a pet's eye unless directed by a veterinarian.

FALLS – see TRAUMA, page 56.

FISHHOOKS

Fishhooks are an obvious hazard if your dog is nearby when anyone is fishing. In addition, dogs sometimes scavenge through storage areas where they are drawn to hooks and lures and often chew on them because of residual odors from the fish or bait. Often hooks become lodged in a dog's lips or feet.

I. Symptoms (some or all may be present)
A. Portion of hook lodged in skin
B. Pawing at mouth or salivating
C. Limping

II. First-Aid Materials
A. Muzzle
B. Elizabethan collar
C. Wire cutters
D. Protective eye wear
E. Antibiotic ointment (e.g., Polysporin®)

III. First Aid
A. **If the hook has entered past the barb, do not try to pull the fishhook out of the dog.** The barb will cause severe tearing.
B. If the dog has swallowed the hook and there is fishing line extending outside the dog's mouth, do not pull on the line. Cut the line 6 inches from the dog's mouth, and try to keep the dog from swallowing the end of the line. Seek veterinary help immediately to have the hook extracted.
C. If the hook is lodged somewhere other than the dog's mouth, apply a muzzle to the dog. (Except never muzzle a dog that may have difficulty breathing, has a flat face or small nostrils, or is vomiting.)
D. If the hook is in the dog's mouth, apply an Elizabethan collar to prevent the dog from pawing at the hook.
E. If the hook has not gone all the way through, it will need to be extracted by a veterinarian to minimize damage.
F. If the hook has gone all the way through and is sticking out the other side past the barb, use wire cutters to cut the back end of the hook, and then extract the hook by moving it through the rest of the way. Make sure you use protective eye wear before cutting the hook. Do not try to cut off the barb and back the hook out the way it went in because many hooks have secondary

barbs that you might not see, and these can cause severe tearing.

G. After the hook has been removed, clean the wound with soap and water, and apply antibiotic ointment. If the wound is in the bottom of the foot, apply a wrap. See Wrapping a Wound on page 16.

H. Even if you have been successful at removing the hook and cleaning the wound, have your dog checked by a veterinarian as soon as possible.

FRACTURES

The most common cause of fractures is trauma. Regardless of the cause, the single most important thing you can do to help the dog is RESTRICT ACTIVITY. By restricting activity immediately, you decrease the chances of the pet worsening the injury.

Many fractures are the result of severe trauma, such as getting hit by a car. An emergency involving a fracture should be treated with great urgency because the pet may have life-threatening internal injuries not immediately evident. If a fracture is compound (open to the air) or severely fragmented, the pet can hemorrhage and quickly go into shock.

I. Symptoms (some or all may be present)

A. Dogs usually will not bear weight on a fractured leg.

B. Limbs may appear swollen.

C. Fractures are usually painful and do not improve with time.

D. Fractures of the ribs may be associated with difficult breathing.

II. First-Aid Materials

A. Gauze sponges and roll gauze

B. Tape

C. Muzzle

D. Towels

E. Blanket

F. 2-liter soda bottle filled with warm water

G. Plywood board cut to fit your dog and your car

III. First Aid

A. Because fractures are painful, you may wish to use a muzzle to prevent being bitten when you move your dog. However, use a muzzle only if the dog is not having difficulty breathing and has

not been vomiting. If at any time the dog has difficulty breathing, remove the muzzle. Also, do not use a muzzle if your dog has a flat face (e.g., a pug, boxer, English bulldog, etc.).

B. Keep the dog still. If necessary, wrap the pet in a towel or blanket to restrict its movements.
C. Keep any open wounds covered with gauze and secure with tape.
D. If an open wound is bleeding profusely, apply pressure over that area.
E. Treat for shock: see pages 79-80.
F. Seek veterinary help immediately. Plan the transportation to the veterinarian carefully to minimize movement of the dog. See *Transporting a Dog with Fractures or Back Injuries* on pages 13-14.
G. Monitor the dog's vital signs (temperature, pulse and respirations).
H. Observe for other injuries.

FROSTBITE

A dog's coat will not protect it from extreme cold. When temperatures or windchill fall below freezing, it is important that your dog has shelter. As with people, frostbite occurs when the extreme cold restricts blood flow to an appendage and thereby causes the tissue to die. The damage is frequently permanent. Frostbite may involve any appendage, but in dogs most often it affects the tips of the ears. Exposure that causes frostbite can also cause death by freezing.

I. **Symptoms (one or both may be present)**
A. The ears or appendages may appear reddened and blistered. The symptoms may not be evident immediately after exposure to cold but will appear in a short period of time.
B. Frostbitten tissue will eventually turn dark and slough or scar.

II. **First-Aid Materials**
A. Contact-lens saline solution
B. Antibiotic ointment (e.g., Polysporin®)
C. 2-liter soda bottle

III. **First Aid**
A. If frostbite is suspected, immediately warm the ears or extremities in tepid water. Do not use hot water.

B. If damage has already occurred, gently rinse the affected area in saline or water and apply antibiotic ointment.
C. If the dog is chilled (hypothermic), fill a 2-liter soda bottle with warm water (not hot water), and place the bottle against the dog as illustrated on page 80. See pages 58-59 for further information and instruction regarding hypothermia.
D. Contact the dog's veterinarian for further instructions.

GUNSHOT WOUNDS

If your dog is ever a victim of a shooting, you need to control the bleeding as fast as possible. Also, you may need to treat the dog for shock.

I. First-Aid Materials
A. Clean towel
B. Gauze sponges
C. Nonstick adhesive tape
D. Nonstick bandages
E. Gauze wrap

II. First Aid
A. Locate the source of bleeding.
B. DO NOT attempt to remove pellets or bullets.
C. Using a clean towel or sterile sponges, apply direct pressure to the area of bleeding for 5-10 minutes. If the bleeding does not stop, you may apply a wrap using the following procedure:
(1) Press nonstick bandage to wound.
(2) Secure nonstick bandage to wound by wrapping gauze around the dog's leg or body. The gauze should be snug but not tight. The wrap should not restrict the dog's circulation or breathing.
(3) Secure the gauze by applying adhesive tape to the wrap.
(4) Monitor the pet for any evidence of swelling to the limb below the wrap. If swelling occurs, then the wrap is too tight, and you should loosen it immediately. If the dog's breathing is hindered, also loosen or remove the wrap.
D. For future reference, note the amount of blood loss.
E. If the bleeding was difficult to stop, do not attempt to clean the wound or apply antibiotic ointment because the clot may be disrupted and severe hemorrhage may resume.

F. Confine the dog to prevent activity.
G. Treat the dog for shock as directed on pages 79-80.
H. Call your veterinarian immediately.

HEAD TILT

The most common cause of a dog having its head tilted is an inner ear problem. Both the underlying condition and the head tilt often result in disorientation, loss of balance and coordination, and sometimes an inability to self-feed.

I. Problems/Conditions with that Symptom
A. Inner ear infections and swelling
B. Trauma
C. Cancers/tumors
D. Foreign body in ear
E. Blood clot

II. First-Aid Materials
A. Cotton balls

III. First Aid
A. Look in the ear to see whether there is a discharge or something blocking the ear canal. Gently wipe any debris from the ear canal using a cotton ball. If the debris is difficult to remove, seek veterinary assistance to prevent further damage and infection.
B. If the dog is disoriented or appears to have a loss of balance or coordination, block off stairways and restrict the pet's activity. Carry or help the dog out to go to the bathroom four times per day.
C. If the dog shows no sign of nausea, offer food and water by hand feeding; the dog's condition may prevent it from eating and drinking out of a bowl.
D. Seek veterinary care as soon as possible.

HEART DISEASE

Heart disease is a common occurrence in dogs. The disease may be a result of a birth defect, heartworm disease, infection, heart muscle disease, valve disease, or aging. Regardless of the cause, the

condition may be very debilitating. Recognizing symptoms early and getting help as soon as possible may improve the outcome.

I. Symptoms (some or all may be present)
A. Coughing
B. Labored respirations (or gasping)
C. Weakness
D. Blue-tinged gums or tongue
E. Enlarged abdomen
F. Accelerated or depressed heart rate
G. Loss of consciousness

II. First-Aid Materials
A. Two 2-liter soda bottles
B. Blanket

III. First Aid
A. If the pet is unconscious and does not have a heartbeat or is not breathing, begin CPR immediately: see pages 18-19.
B. Keep the dog calm. Do not use excessive restraint or move the dog more than necessary.
C. Keep the dog warm with the blanket and with the 2-liter soda bottles filled with warm water placed against the dog's body.
D. Call your veterinarian.

HEAT STROKE OR HYPERTHERMIA

Heat stroke is a common occurrence during the warmer months of the year. Dogs are prone to overheating because they do not sweat. Other factors such as obesity, advanced age, infancy and poor ventilation also predispose dogs to hyperthermia.

I. Symptoms (some or all may be present)
A. Panting
B. Weakness or collapse
C. Elevated temperature (from 105 to 110 degrees Fahrenheit)
D. Vomiting, diarrhea and/or lack of urine production
E. Seizures

II. First-Aid Materials
A. 2-liter soda bottle

B. Towel
C. Thermometer
D. Lubricating jelly (e.g., K-Y™ Brand) or petroleum jelly

III. First Aid
A. Take the dog's temperature. (See page 17.)
B. If temperature is greater than 106 degrees, immerse the dog (except for its head) in cold water.
C. Monitor the dog's temperature every 2 minutes to observe any change.
D. Stop the cooling process once the dog's temperature drops to 104 degrees. Do not wait until the temperature falls to normal because the dog's temperature may continue to drop.
E. If the temperature falls below 100 degrees Fahrenheit, keep the pet warm by covering it with a towel and by placing a 2-liter soda bottle filled with warm water (not hot water) against the dog.
F. Contact a veterinarian immediately to prevent shock and other complications.

HIT BY CAR AND TRAUMA

In a situation involving serious trauma, such as being hit by a car, immediate care may be crucial. In addition to the damage caused by the physical impact, there is a high risk that the animal will go into shock. If your dog is able to walk after being hit by a car, the dog may arrive home showing a varying degree of symptoms.

I. Symptoms (some or all may be present)
A. Weakness
B. Lameness
C. Difficulty breathing
D. Bleeding
E. Pale or purple gums
F. Collapse

II. First-Aid Materials
A. Blanket and/or towels
B. Gauze
C. Tape
D. Muzzle
E. Contact-lens saline solution

F.   Antibiotic ointment (e.g., Polysporin®)

G.   Plywood board cut to fit your dog and your car

III. First Aid

A.   If the dog is having difficulty breathing, keep it upright and do not apply any unnecessary or overly-restrictive restraint. Because fractures are painful, you may wish to use a muzzle to prevent being bitten when you move your dog. However, use a muzzle only if the dog is not having difficulty breathing and has not been vomiting. If at any time the dog has difficulty breathing, remove the muzzle. Also, do not use a muzzle if your dog has a flat face (e.g., a pug, boxer, English bulldog, etc.).

B.   Keep the dog still. If necessary, wrap the pet in a towel or blanket to restrict its movements.

C.   If an open wound is bleeding profusely, apply pressure over that area. Do not attempt to wash the wound, and do not apply any ointment.

D.   Seal any open chest wound using a piece of plastic wrap, and then cover the plastic wrap with a bandage. Make sure that the bandage is not so tight that it restricts the dog's breathing.

E.   Treat for shock: see pages 79-80.

F.   Seek veterinary help immediately. Plan the transportation to the veterinarian carefully to minimize movement of the dog. See *Transporting a Dog with Fractures or Back Injuries*, pages 13-14.

G.   For minor wounds, while awaiting veterinary care, wash with water or saline solution, apply antibiotic ointment and cover with a gauze bandage. If there are other serious injuries, do not treat minor wounds if it will delay other medical attention.

H.   For additional information and instruction about specific injuries, see the appropriate section(s) of this book (e.g., fractures, bleeding, wound care, lacerations, wrapping a wound).

HOT SPOTS
(ACUTE MOIST DERMATITIS)

Hot spots, also called acute moist dermatitis, is a common skin disorder that occurs in all breeds of dogs. Hot spots initially appear as reddened areas on the skin that are extremely painful and itchy to the dog. Typically, the dog will lick and chew at the hot spot areas until the hair is missing and the area is raw or bloody. Fleas and/or allergies may make the condition worse.

I. **Symptoms (some or all may be present)**
A. Red area under hair or on skin
B. Dog licking or chewing at skin
C. Pain over affected area
D. Hair loss or sticky hair

II. **First-Aid Materials**
A. Scissors
B. Antibiotic ointment (e.g., Polysporin®)

III. **First Aid**
A. Because hot spots are painful, you may wish to use a muzzle to prevent being bitten when you treat your dog. However, use a muzzle only if the dog is not having difficulty breathing and has not been vomiting. If at any time the dog has difficulty breathing, remove the muzzle. Also, do not use a muzzle if your dog has a flat face (e.g., a pug, boxer, English bulldog, etc.).
B. Carefully trim the hair away from affected areas with scissors.
C. Cleanse with warm water and soap.
D. Apply antibiotic ointment.
E. Repeat steps C and D every 6 to 8 hours.
F. If the dog persists in licking or chewing the affected areas, apply an Elizabethan collar. See page 21.
G. Seek veterinary attention for additional medication.

HYPOTHERMIA

Hypothermia (i.e., chilling) is a condition caused by exposure to cold. It may or may not be accompanied by frostbite. If your dog stays outdoors in cold weather, make sure there is adequate shelter (e.g., a barn or a garage). Never leave your dog outside unprotected in temperatures below 32 degrees Fahrenheit. Even in temperatures above freezing, your dog can become hypothermic if there is wind or rain. Also, your dog's general health, age, and build may affect its susceptibility. If left untreated, hypothermia can be fatal.

I. **Symptoms (some or all may be present)**
A. In early stages the dog may be shivering.
B. In later stages the dog will become stuporous, depressed, confused or even comatose.

C.   The body temperature will fall below 99 degrees Fahrenheit.

II.   **First-Aid Materials**
A.   Thermometer
B.   Lubricating jelly (e.g., K-Y™ Brand) or petroleum jelly
C.   2-liter soda bottles
D.   Towels and/or blanket

III.   **First Aid**
A.   Bring the dog into the house or into some other warm area.
B.   Take the dog's temperature. (See page 17.)
C.   If the temperature is below 98 degrees Fahrenheit, rewarm the dog carefully by placing a 2-liter soda bottle filled with warm water against the dog's body. (See illustration on page 80.)
D.   Check the dog's temperature every 5-10 minutes. Keep the dog warm by keeping it covered with a blanket, even if its temperature returns to normal.
E.   Because of the danger of shock, seek immediate veterinary care.

IBUPROFEN TOXICITY – see page 98.

INFECTIONS AND FEVER

Infections and fever are unpredictable when left unattended. Some can become overwhelming and cause long-term complications or death. Always treat infections and fever as soon as possible.

I.   **Symptoms of Infections and Fever (some or all may be present)**
A.   Pain and swelling at site of infection
B.   Elevated temperature
C.   Listlessness
D.   Other general signs of illness such as vomiting, diarrhea, coughing, sneezing, and loss of appetite

II.   **Home Care**
A.   Use all medications as prescribed by the veterinarian.
B.   Do not deviate from the dosage or the time interval on the label.
C.   Use all antibiotics until gone, unless directed otherwise. Sporadic use of antibiotics can cause bacteria to become resistant to treatment.

D. Take the dog's temperature daily to monitor progress. See page 17.

III. Veterinary Care
A. When you suspect your dog has an infection or fever, contact your veterinarian immediately; antibiotics may be necessary.
B. If the dog's condition does not improve while on medication, contact your veterinarian. It may be necessary to change medications or to perform a culture to identify the problem.

INNER EAR OR VESTIBULAR DISEASE

The inner ear and vestibular system help control balance, posture and head position. Any injury, infection or inflammation in the ear can cause stroke-like symptoms. Early treatment is critical to prevent further damage and possible infection.

I.   Symptoms (some or all may be present)
A. Tilted head
B. Disorientation/confusion
C. Stumbling and loss of coordination or balance
D. Walking in circles
E. Eyes involuntarily moving from side to side

II. First-Aid Materials
A. Cotton balls

III. First Aid
A. Look in the ear to see whether there is a discharge or something blocking the ear canal. Gently wipe any debris from the ear canal using a cotton ball. If the debris is difficult to remove, seek veterinary assistance to prevent further damage and infection.
B. If the dog is disoriented or appears to have a loss of balance or coordination, block off stairways and restrict the pet's activity. Carry or help the dog out to go to the bathroom four times per day.
C. If the dog shows no sign of nausea, offer food and water by hand feeding; the dog's condition may prevent it from eating and drinking out of a bowl.
D. Seek veterinary care as soon as possible.

INSECT INGESTION

Ingestion of an occasional fly, mosquito or lightning bug is typically harmless. However, some insects are toxic (e.g., the monarch butterfly), though these are the exceptions. Frequently with insect ingestion, the primary risk is bites and stings in the dog's mouth.

I. Symptoms (some or all may be present)
A. Salivation from mouth irritation (from bites or stings)
B. Weakness
C. Vomiting
D. Diarrhea
E. Disorientation
F. Difficulty breathing
G. Seizures

II. First-Aid Materials
A. Hydrogen peroxide
B. Eyedropper

III. First Aid
A. If the dog's mouth seems irritated (e.g., if the dog is salivating or rubbing its mouth), flush the dog's mouth with fresh water.
B. If possible, identify the type of insect (to assist in appropriate veterinary treatment).
C. If the pet shows any signs of illness from ingestion, immediately induce vomiting (unless the dog is unconscious, having difficulty breathing, or is in a stupor). See Inducing Vomiting on page 17.

INTESTINAL PARASITES

Intestinal parasites, which include worms and protozoa, can cause serious illness if untreated. In general, most infestations are mild at first but then become serious as time progresses. If parasites are left untreated, fatal anemia from chronic blood loss and life-threatening malnutrition can develop. It is important to have a stool sample checked under the microscope for worm eggs. If any eggs are present, your veterinarian can prescribe the proper medication.

The most common parasites in dogs include roundworms, tapeworms, hookworms and whipworms. Protozoa infestations include coccidia, giardia and cryptosporidium. Some can be spread to people.

I. **Symptoms (some or all may be present)**
A. Weight loss
B. Diarrhea or soft stools
C. Blood and/or mucus in stools
D. Listlessness
E. Vomiting
F. Dull hair coat
G. Pot-bellied appearance
H. Worms in the stool or under the dog's tail

II. **Home Prevention**
A. Clean the yard of stools at least once per day.
B. Practice good flea control. Fleas spread one type of tapeworm.
C. Never feed a dog raw meat.
D. Provide clean, fresh water for your outdoor dog because outside water may contain infectious protozoa or bacteria.
E. If you see any worms in the stool, contact your veterinarian.

III. **Veterinary Care**
A. Have a stool specimen examined by a veterinarian at least twice per year.
B. Use worm medications as directed.

LAMENESS

I. **Problems/Conditions with that Symptom**
A. Fractures
B. Sprains, torn ligaments and dislocations
C. Bite wounds
D. Bruises
E. Foot-pad injury (e.g., splinter, puncture, laceration)
F. Torn toenail
G. Back or neck injury (including slipped disc)

II. **First-Aid Materials**
A. Gauze sponges and roll gauze
B. Tape
C. Tweezers
D. Antibiotic ointment (e.g., Polysporin®)

III. **First Aid**
A. Restrict activity and keep the dog still to prevent further injury.

B.   Use a muzzle to prevent being bitten when treating your dog. However, do NOT muzzle a dog that is having difficulty breathing or has been vomiting. If at any time the dog has difficulty breathing, remove the muzzle. Also, do not use a muzzle if your dog has a flat face (e.g., a pug, boxer, English bulldog, etc.) or has small or underdeveloped nostrils.

C.   Attempt to identify the cause of the lameness.

D.   If lameness is caused by a splinter or similar foreign object, use tweezers to remove the object. Apply antibiotic ointment.

E.   For any minor wound where bleeding control is not a problem, apply antibiotic ointment and keep the wound covered with gauze and secure with tape.

F.   If the dog has a wound that is bleeding, apply pressure. (For additional information, see Bleeding on pages 29-31 and Wrapping a Wound on page 16.)

G.   If the cause of the lameness is a serious injury or if there are other symptoms, monitor the dog's vital signs (temperature, pulse, and respirations). See page 17.

H.   Observe for other injuries.

I.   Call a veterinarian for additional instructions.

LOCKED DOGS

When dogs breed, it is normal for them to become locked together during copulation. This occurs because the bulb of the dog's penis enlarges and the female dog's vulva locks around it. Copulation may take up to 20 minutes for completion.

I.   Symptoms (one or both may be present)

A.   Male dog and female dog unable to separate after copulation.

B.   Male and female dog may be connected tail to tail when the male dog dismounts.

II.   First Aid

A.   Do nothing. Do not disturb or try to separate the animals. Dogs that are forced apart may experience damage to their genitalia. The dogs will eventually separate on their own.

B.   To discourage pet overpopulation, spay or neuter your dog.

LOSS OF COORDINATION/LOSS OF BALANCE

Loss of coordination or balance may result from a variety of causes. Often an inner ear problem will cause loss of balance, but many other disease processes, including encephalitis or a herniated disc (slipped disc), can cause that symptom as well. Because the origin of the problem may be any of several conditions or diseases, you should contact a veterinarian immediately.

I. Problems/Conditions with that Symptom
A. Inner ear infections and swelling
B. Trauma
C. Cancers/tumors
D. Foreign object in ear
E. Poisoning or extreme illness

II. First-Aid Materials
A. Cotton balls

III. First Aid
A. Look in the ear to see whether there is a discharge or something blocking the ear canal. Gently wipe any debris from the ear canal using a cotton ball. If the debris is difficult to remove, seek veterinary assistance to prevent further damage and infection.
B. If the dog is disoriented or is losing its balance or coordination, block off stairways and restrict the pet's activity. Carry or help the dog out to go to the bathroom four times per day.
C. If the dog shows no sign of nausea, offer food and water by hand feeding; the dog's condition may prevent it from eating and drinking out of a bowl.
D. Seek veterinary care as soon as possible.

LOW BLOOD SUGAR (HYPOGLYCEMIA)

Low blood sugar can occur as a complication in insulin overdose or from insulinoma cancer. With puppies, perhaps the most common cause is being food deprived or being poorly nourished. Hypoglycemia is life threatening, so prompt attention is critical.

I. Symptoms (some or all may be present)
A. Weakness
B. Depression
C. Shaking
D. Seizures
E. Coma

II. First-Aid Materials
A. Corn syrup
B. Dog food

III. First Aid
A. Give the dog 1 teaspoon of corn syrup. Rub the corn syrup on the dog's gums if the pet will not swallow it.
B. Try to get the dog to eat a meal.
C. Seek veterinary care. The dog may temporarily improve only to have its sugar drop once more.

LUNG DISEASE AND RESPIRATORY DISTRESS

A dog suffering from lung disease or respiratory distress does not receive enough oxygen to be comfortable or function normally. The condition may be caused by many disease processes, including pneumonia, trauma, heart disease, heartworm disease and cancer. The condition is life threatening; contact a veterinarian immediately.

I. Symptoms (some or all may be present)
A. The dog may take short, shallow or rapid breaths or may pant.
B. The dog's gum or tongue color may be purple, blue, or pale.
C. The pet may be able only to sit upright with its elbows pointed outward; the dog may not be able to lie flat.
D. The dog may be depressed, but sometimes restless, due to the lack of oxygen.

II. First Aid
A. Avoid stressing the pet. The least amount of stress may precipitate a crisis when the pet cannot breathe properly.
B. Do not monitor vital signs.
C. Plan the handling of the dog to minimize excitement. Never hold the dog tightly.

D. Keep the dog in an upright position (i.e., belly down). Never lay the dog on its back or side because those positions make breathing more difficult by putting extra pressure on the chest.
E. Contact a veterinarian immediately.

NOSEBLEED

Dogs can get nosebleeds from several sources. Trauma, immune disorders, tick-borne diseases, cancer, and rat bait poisonings can result in nosebleeds. It is important to look for other symptoms to help discover the cause of the nosebleed. Also note whether the bleeding is coming from one or both nostrils.

I. **Symptoms (some or all may be present)**
A. Blood crusted around nostril(s)
B. Blood accumulating under skin, in the nasal area, looking like a bruise
C. Blood in the dog's urine, feces or vomitus
D. Weakness
E. Pale gums
F. Labored breathing
G. Distended abdomen
H. Sneezing

II. **First-Aid Materials**
A. Clean towel
B. Gauze sponges

III. **First Aid**
A. Restrict all activity
B. If there is breathing difficulty, refer to page 33, and seek veterinary attention immediately.
C. Do not clean the dog's face if that worsens the bleeding.
D. If the bleeding was not caused by trauma and the bleeding stops on its own, contact a veterinarian to determine the cause.

PARALYSIS

Paralysis, when it occurs, typically involves the loss of function of the dog's leg(s). Some causes include trauma, herniated disc

disease, infections, embolisms and cancers. Most often paralysis is associated with damage to the spinal cord.

I.   Symptoms (some or all may be present)
A. Dragging one or more legs or toes
B. Back or neck pain
C. Reluctance to move
D. Disorientation
E. Partial or complete loss of the ability to move

II.   First-Aid Materials
A. Muzzle
B. Blanket or plywood board (cut to fit your dog and your car)

III. First Aid and Transportation
A. Paralysis is typically associated with injury to the spinal cord. Immediate veterinary care is essential. Proper transport of the dog to a veterinarian is extremely important--see D and E below.
B. Keep the dog quiet, and restrict all activity.
C. If the dog is in pain, use a muzzle to prevent being bitten, but use it only if the dog is not having difficulty breathing and has not been vomiting. If at any time the dog has difficulty breathing, remove the muzzle. Also, do not use a muzzle if your dog has a flat face (e.g., a pug, boxer, English bulldog, etc.).
D. **If there is any chance your dog has damage to its spinal cord:**
(1) Obtain a plywood board to use as a stretcher. Slide the dog onto the board with as little movement as possible. If the dog's back or neck is injured, excess movement could cause permanent damage. If a board is not available, and you judge that delaying transport is more of a risk than moving the dog, try using a blanket or towel as a stretcher instead.
(2) Ideally, place the plywood board with the dog on it into your vehicle. If the board will not fit, slide the dog off the board and onto the seat with as little movement of the pet as possible. If you have used a blanket or towel rather than a board, keep the blanket or towel under the dog when you put the pet into the car.
(3) Pack blankets around the dog to keep the pet warm. If you are concerned that the dog may slide off the seat onto the floor, pack the floor area with a pillow or blankets. Place one or two 2-liter soda bottles filled with warm water (not hot water) against the dog. See illustration on page 80.

67

E. **If you are certain there is no damage to the spinal cord:**

(1) If the dog does not have a spinal-cord injury (i.e., no neck or back problem) but is weak or paralyzed in its hind quarters, you can place a towel under the dog's abdomen for use as a sling to support the dog. See illustration below.

(2) If the dog does not have a spinal-cord injury but is unable to support weight with either its front or back legs, you may lift and carry the dog to your car by placing one arm under the dog's neck and through the front legs and the other arm under the back third of the abdomen. Be careful not to make the back or neck arch. See illustration on page 11.

(3) Pack blankets around the dog to keep the pet warm. If you are concerned that the dog may slide off the seat onto the floor, pack the floor area with a pillow or blankets. Place one or two 2-liter soda bottles filled with warm water (not hot water) against the dog. See illustrations on page 80.

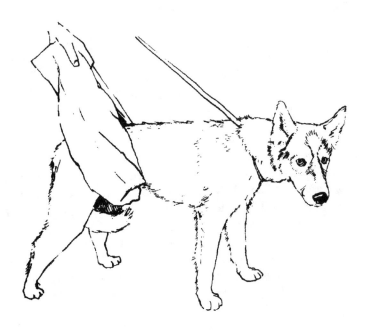

PARVOVIRUS AND CORONAVIRUS

With parvovirus, dogs often die within 24 hours after the onset of symptoms. The virus attacks the lining of the digestive tract causing severe vomiting and bloody diarrhea. Coronavirus infections tend to be slightly less severe than parvovirus but are still often fatal when not treated. Both parvovirus and coronavirus affect young, small and debilitated dogs most severely. Dogs that are infected with either virus can be contagious to other dogs for two weeks, and the virus can remain in the environment for years; proper disinfecting is required to ensure that healthy dogs entering the same environment do not become infected.

Vaccinations can prevent this disease. Consult your veterinarian regarding vaccinations and other precautions.

I. Symptoms (some or all may be present)
A. Loss of appetite
B. Depression
C. Vomiting
D. Watery diarrhea that is often bloody and usually foul-smelling
E. Pale gums
F. Shivering
G. Rapid decline in physical condition
H. Collapse

II. First-Aid Materials
A. Plain yogurt
B. Boiled hamburger
C. Plain cooked rice

III. First Aid
A. Seek veterinary care immediately. Parvovirus is often fatal within 24 hours from the onset of symptoms.
B. If there is no vomiting, feed your dog 2 to 3 tablespoons of plain yogurt. DO NOT administer human medications for diarrhea; they often contain salicylates that can react with other medicines and complicate a digestive upset.
C. If you are still delayed from receiving veterinary help, repeat Step B every 4 to 6 hours for adult dogs and every 2 to 4 hours for puppies less than 14 weeks old.
D. Withhold food for 2-4 hours if diarrhea is present and if there is no other symptom of illness. Withhold both food and water if

the dog is also vomiting, but do not withhold water for more than 2 hours. Do not withhold water if the dog is not vomiting. The time period for withholding food should be based on whether your pet is a normal, healthy adult versus a puppy, an elderly dog or a dog with any special or compromising conditions. If your dog has diabetes or any other type of illness or medical condition, consult your veterinarian first before withholding food and water.

E. When you do resume feeding your dog, the best home remedy for diarrhea is to prepare a 50/50 mixture of boiled hamburger (drain off the water and fat) and plain cooked rice. Appropriate feedings are as follows:
(1) 1/4 cup of the mixture 4 times per day for small dogs,
(2) 1/2 cup of the mixture 4 times per day for medium dogs,
(3) 3/4 cup of the mixture 4 times per day for large dogs.
Your veterinarian may wish to adjust the servings or may recommend a prescription diet instead.

F. Note the frequency and substance of the diarrhea.

G. Parvovirus is often fatal, and professional veterinary care is critical for your dog's survival. The above procedures are appropriate while waiting for professional help, but they are not sufficient to save your dog.

PENIS SHEATH DISCHARGE (BALANOPOSTHITIS)

Inflammation in the sheath surrounding the dog's penis (balanoposthitis) is common and is usually not cause for alarm, but the condition must be treated properly. It may be caused by foreign debris, a laceration, trauma or even a tumor. Dogs are prone to this type of inflammation and infection because there is a natural pocket or cavity in the sheath. When infection occurs, there is generally a cloudy discharge.

I.   Symptoms (one or both may be present)
A. Cloudy, thick discharge from sheath
B. Dog licking sheath

II.   Problems/Conditions with that Symptom
A. Foreign debris in the sheath

B. Laceration in the penis area
C. Trauma to the penis/sheath
D. Tumor in the penis/sheath

III. First-Aid Materials
A. Antibiotic ointment (e.g., Polysporin®)

IV. First Aid
A. Wipe discharge away from sheath.
B. Apply antibiotic ointment into sheath opening.
C. Seek veterinary care.

PORCUPINE QUILLS

When a dog startles a porcupine, or worse yet tries to attack one, the dog may end up with quills embedded in its face, mouth, tongue, and/or throat. The porcupine's tail is its defense against attack. The tail has numerous barbed quills that, with a quick motion from the porcupine, become firmly embedded into the victim's skin. The barbs are painful and are difficult to remove.

I. Symptoms (one or more may be present)
A. Quills protruding from the face, mouth, or body.
B. Pawing at face or mouth.
C. Difficulty swallowing
D. Drooling or coughing

II. First-Aid Materials
A. Pliers
B. Antibiotic Ointment

III. First Aid
A. Do not attempt to remove the quills if they are embedded into the tongue, throat or eyes--seek veterinary assistance immediately.
B. If there are only 1 or 2 quills, then you might attempt removal. (If there are more, see your veterinarian right away for removal under anesthesia and for pain management.)
C. Grab the quill at the base with the pliers, and let the dog jerk away while you hold firmly to the pliers/quill.
D. Treat the site with antibiotic ointment.

PROTRUDING ORGANS

The things that most commonly protrude in a dog are a prolapsed rectum, an exposed prolapsed penis (see Protruding Penis on page 73 for treatment), a traumatic hernia with bowels exposed, and a popped-out eye. All of the above require immediate attention because these organs can dry out quickly, causing permanent damage.

I. Symptoms (one or both may be present)

A. Most of these conditions can be recognized by observing the misplacement of the specific organ.

B. A prolapsed rectum may occur intermittently; the rectum may protrude only during times of straining, such as during a bowel movement.

II. First-Aid Materials

A. Towel and/or gauze sponges

B. Contact-lens saline solution

C. Antibiotic ointment (e.g., Polysporin®)

III. First Aid

A. Contact a veterinarian immediately.

B. For a protruding rectum, soak a towel or gauze sponges with saline solution and place on the rectum or apply several drops of saline directly onto the rectum to prevent the organ from becoming dehydrated. Also apply antibiotic ointment to help soothe the discomfort and prevent infection.

C. For protruding organs in general, soak a towel or gauze sponges with saline solution and apply to any area of protrusion. This will keep the organs from becoming dehydrated and improve the prognosis. Also, by covering the protrusion, you will help prevent the dog from mutilating itself. With a disembowelment in particular, dogs will often chew on the exposed organs.

D. If the dog's eye is protruding, rinse the eye in saline every five minutes until a veterinarian can be reached. Do not apply pressure directly to the eye.

E. Use an Elizabethan collar if the dog is attempting to chew or scratch at the injury. See page 21.

F. Treat for shock: see pages 79-80.

G. Seek veterinary help immediately.

PROTRUDING PENIS (PARAPHIMOSIS)

Male dogs have a sheath that covers the penis. During mating or when the male dog is similarly aroused, the penis comes out from inside the sheath. Occasionally, hairs from the sheath get caught on the penis and prevent it from returning to the sheath. When this happens, the penis may swell, have its blood supply constricted by the sheath, and dry out.

I. **Symptoms (some or all may be present)**
A. Penis protruding from sheath
B. Swollen penis
C. Discolored (dark) penis
D. Dog licking genitals

II. **First-Aid Materials**
A. Contact-lens saline solution
B. Antibiotic ointment (e.g., Polysporin®)
C. Water-soluble lubricating jelly (e.g., K-Y™ Brand)

III. **First Aid**
A. Rinse penis with saline solution to remove any debris.
B. Apply antibiotic ointment to penis to prevent infection.
C. Apply water-soluble lubricating jelly to penis.
D. Gently remove any hairs that may be preventing retraction of the penis into the sheath. Then gently pull the sheath over the penis.
E. If the penis will not return to the sheath, immediate veterinary care is necessary to prevent the penis from drying out and dying. If there is any delay is obtaining veterinary care, be certain to reapply antibiotic ointment to the penis every 30 minutes. Use an Elizabethan collar to prevent the dog from licking and chewing.

PUPPY EMERGENCIES

Immediately after adoption, it is your responsibility (not the responsibility of the shelter, pet store or breeder) to ensure that your puppy's needs are met. It is important to have a new puppy examined by a veterinarian to look for birth defects or underlying illness that could hinder your puppy's ability to thrive. Your veterinarian will also provide advice on how to overcome behavioral frustrations that your puppy may experience, such as crying, barking and chewing.

"Special considerations" refers to conditions that may complicate emergency situations. With a puppy, the following special considerations apply:

A. Because of a puppy's small body size, it has little reserve to support itself during an illness.
B. Puppies have immature immune systems that are inadequate for fighting infections after the puppies are weaned from their mothers. Make sure your puppy gets timely vaccinations.
C. Because of a puppy's curiosity, it is prone to finding trouble that can result in injury.

The following are some common problems seen in newly adopted puppies. Typically these diseases, once treated, resolve uneventfully, but treatment is necessary, and in fact can be crucial.

I.   Common Puppy Problems
A. Kennel Cough (Bordetella) – Kennel Cough is a bacterial infection that results in bronchitis and causes a dry cough. (See Coughing on pages 40-41.)
B. Intestinal Parasites – See pages 61-62.
C. Digestive upsets due to stress and diet change – See Diarrhea on pages 42-44 and Vomiting on page 90.
D. Behaviorial problems due to change in environment.

II.   Signs of Illness – contact your veterinarian
A. Loss of appetite (see Low Blood Sugar on pages 64-65)
B. Decreased appetite for longer than 1 meal
C. Lethargy, depression or lack of playfulness
D. Fatigues easily
E. Dry gums
F. Pale gums
G. Mucous in stool
H. Blood in stool
I. Stool that is soft or watery
J. More than 3-4 bowel movements per day
K. Shivering
L. Cloudy nasal discharge
M. Collapse (see Low Blood Sugar on pages 64-65)
N. Cough, especially if combined with any symptoms above or if the cough becomes productive.

RAISING ORPHAN PUPPIES

When puppies have been abandoned or when the mother does not nurse her puppies, the puppies will need special care if they are to survive. Raising orphan puppies can be very rewarding but demands much time, motivation, and devotion. Unlike adult dogs, puppies have little body reserve and need highly regimented feeding and care schedules.

I. **Materials Needed**
A. Cotton balls
B. Light bulb or heat lamp
C. Pet nurser
D. Eyedropper
E. Formula
F. Scale for weighing
G. Thermometer

II. **Hygiene/Husbandry**
A. The puppy's nest area should be cleaned three times daily to prevent disease. Bed the area with newspaper or towels.
B. Store all formula as directed on the label to prevent spoilage.
C. Chilling is one of the leading causes of death among newborns. Keep the puppies warm with a heat lamp, heating pad, or hot water bottles. However, take care that the heat source is not too hot, and prepare a box that provides enough room for the puppies to move away from the heat source if they become too hot. Heating pads must be monitored closely to regulate temperature and prevent fire hazard. **Do not place a heating pad or hot water bottle on top of the puppies**.
D. The environmental temperature should be kept at 85-90 degrees from days 1-7. The temperature should be lowered to 80 degrees during week 2. Weeks 3-5, the temperature should be lowered to 75 degrees, then decreased again to 70 degrees at week 6.
E. Urinations and bowel movements must be stimulated after each meal. This is accomplished by moistening a cotton ball with warm water and gently wiping the puppy's bottom and abdomen.
F. Weigh each puppy and take its temperature daily.

III. **Feeding**
A. Use a pet nurser, if available, to feed the puppies. The hole in the nurser should leak milk slowly from the bottle without

pressure. An eyedropper may be used temporarily if a nurser is unavailable.

B. Never feed a chilled puppy; make sure the orphan is warm prior to feeding.

C. Commercial formulas for newborns or infants are recommended over homemade diets. Homemade diets tend to lack balanced nutrition. If a commercial formula is not available, the following can be substituted temporarily:

EMERGENCY FORMULA RECIPE #1
8 oz. homogenized whole milk
1 teaspoon salad oil
2 egg yolks
1 drop infant vitamins

EMERGENCY FORMULA RECIPE # 2
1/3 cup nonfat dried milk
1/4 cup cottage cheese
1/8 cup corn oil
Add enough water to make 2 cups volume
Mix in blender

D. When using a commercially available formula, follow the directions on the label regarding preparation, the frequency of feedings, and the amount to be fed. Whether you are using a commercial formula or a home preparation, the size, age and breed of the puppy will dictate what is appropriate in terms of feeding; contact a veterinarian for advice specific to your puppy's needs. Until you are able to reach a veterinarian for professional advice, use the following guidelines for feeding:

(1) Amount of food per feeding based on size of puppy:
   (a) Puppies weighing 2 oz.: feed 1/2 teaspoon.
   (b) Puppies weighing 4 oz.: feed 1 teaspoon.
   (c) Puppies weighing 8 oz.: feed 2 teaspoons.
   (d) Puppies weighing 16 oz.: feed 4 teaspoons.

(2) Frequency of feeding based on age:
   (a) In the first week of life, feed every 2 hours.
   (b) In the second week of life, feed every 2 to 4 hours.
   (c) In the third week of life, feed every 4 to 6 hours.
   (d) In the fourth week of life, feed every 4 to 6 hours, and begin to mix the formula with canned puppy food. Offer these meals on a flat plate and allow the puppy to play in it to encourage self-feeding.

E. Urinations and bowel movements must be stimulated after each meal. This is accomplished by moistening a cotton ball with warm water and gently wiping the puppy's bottom and abdomen.

F. Overfeeding may cause diarrhea. Consult a veterinarian immediately if diarrhea occurs; puppies dehydrate easily.

IV. Signs of Illness

A. Crying (indicates that the puppies are either hungry, chilled, or sick)

B. Restlessness

C. Loss of appetite

D. Fever

E. Weight loss or lack of weight gain

F. Pot-bellied appearance

G. Vomiting or diarrhea

RAT POISON – see page 100.

SCRATCHING SKIN/ IRRITATED SKIN

I. Problems/Conditions with that Symptom

A. Contact with plant resins

B. Frostbite

C. Burns

D. Abrasions

E. Bites and stings (e.g., insects, spiders, snakes)

F. Allergies

G. Fleas, lice and/or mites

H. Drug reactions

II. First-Aid Materials

A. Moisturizing shampoo

B. Elizabethan collar

III. First Aid

A. Shampooing the pet will likely provide temporary relief from its symptoms. Use a shampoo for dogs (moisturizing shampoo is best). While restraining the dog, lather the pet and let stand for 15-20 minutes. Rinse well with lukewarm tap water. Let the coat

dry naturally. Consult your veterinarian for the proper type of shampoo and for specific instructions.

B. If the dog continues to bite or scratch itself, you may need to apply an Elizabethan collar to prevent the dog from causing more damage to the skin. See page 21 on how to make and use an Elizabethan collar.

C. Seek veterinary help as soon as possible to give more permanent relief from the irritation. Until the underlying cause is properly diagnosed and treated, your emergency care will likely provide only temporary relief.

SEIZURES

Seizures are common phenomena in dogs. They can be caused by a number of problems, including blood sugar imbalances (sometimes from diabetes), head trauma, various poisons or a buildup of wastes in the dog's circulation (as a result of organ failure). Some seizures may be hereditary in nature.

Seizures are frightening events to watch. Try to stay calm so that you are best able to tend to your dog's needs.

I.   Symptoms (some or all may be present)
A.   Confusion prior to the onset
B.   Lack of awareness of its surroundings, including unresponsiveness to the owner
C.   Distressed barking/crying
D.   Loss of bladder and/or bowel control
E.   Twitching or convulsing
F.   Collapse
G.   After the seizure has ended, the dog may be confused, uncoordinated and possibly blind for minutes or even hours.

II.   First Aid
A.   Note the time on a clock to measure the duration of the seizure.
B.   If the seizure lasts more than 2 minutes, get veterinary help immediately; the condition may be life-threatening.
C.   Move any objects that could cause the dog injury.
D.   Block any stairways.
E.   Never place your fingers in a dog's mouth during a seizure.
F.   If the seizure stops and the dog appears lifeless, refer to the

section of this book on CPR, on pages 18-19.
G. Even if the seizure stops and the pet seems normal afterwards, consult your veterinarian as soon as possible.

SHAKING HEAD/SCRATCHING EARS

I. Problems/Conditions with that Symptom
A. Ear infection
B. Ear mites
C. Trauma (physical injury)
D. Bite wounds
E. Ear hematoma (swelling)
F. Toad poisoning

II. First-Aid Materials
A. Gauze sponges or cotton balls

III. First Aid
A. If there is debris in the ear flap, gently remove it by using a dry cotton ball or gauze sponge, being careful not to pack the debris into the ear canal. Do not use water or hydrogen peroxide because the moisture will promote infection.
B. Consult your veterinarian as soon as possible.

SHOCK

Shock is an event that accompanies some diseases and injuries. Shock occurs when a series of compensatory mechanisms in the body goes awry. The result can be fatal if not treated early. Problems that can cause shock include overwhelming infections, trauma (i.e., physical injury), severe vomiting and diarrhea, blood loss, and any other serious medical situation.

I. Symptoms (some or all may be present)
A. Note that immediately after an injury or other shock-inducing circumstance, the symptoms of shock may be difficult to recognize, but they may develop quickly.
B. The dog may be depressed and/or disoriented.

C. The dog's vital signs may be decreased. Body temperature may fall, breathing may be shallow and pulse may be weak.

D. The dog's feet, tail, and ears may feel cold to the touch.

II. First-Aid Materials

A. 2-liter soda bottle

B. Blanket or towels

C. Thermometer

D. Lubricating jelly (e.g., K-Y™ Brand) or petroleum jelly

III. First Aid

A. Shock is a danger in virtually all medical emergencies. You should treat your dog for shock following any serious trauma, regardless of whether you observe any symptoms.

B. Keep the dog warm by placing a 2-liter soda bottle filled with warm water (not hot water) against the dog. See illustration below. Cover the dog with a towel or blanket.

C. Monitor the dog's vital signs (temperature, pulse and respirations) every 15 minutes and record the information. Try to keep the dog's temperature within the range of 100 to 102.5 degrees Fahrenheit. If the dog's temperature rises above 102.5 degrees Fahrenheit, remove the warm soda bottle. If the dog's temperature falls below 100 degrees, place an additional warm-water soda bottle against the dog, but make sure the water is not hot and make sure the bottle is against the dog and not on top of or underneath the dog. See illustration below.

D. Contact a veterinarian immediately so that anti-shock drugs and intravenous fluids can be administered.

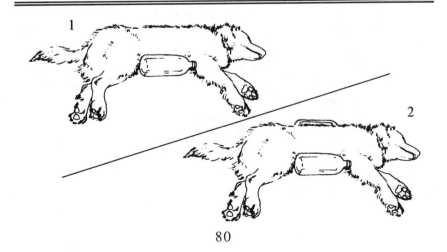

SLIPPED (HERNIATED) DISC DISEASE

Disc disease in dogs causes a variety of symptoms, depending on the location and severity of the condition. Symptoms may range from mild neck or back pain to extreme pain or paralysis. When a disc slips out of place, it applies pressure to the spinal cord, or nerves leading from the cord, creating the pain or paralysis. Mild cases may quickly worsen; prompt veterinary care is needed.

I. **Symptoms (some or all may be present)**
A. Back or neck pain
B. Reluctance to move or participate in routine activities
C. Hesitation to climb or jump
D. Crying when petted or lifted
E. Difficulty lifting head
F. Difficulty eating
G. Lameness
H. Folding under or dragging toes or back legs
I. Hunched appearance when walking
J. Pain during bowel movements
K. Paralysis

II. **First-Aid Materials**
A. Muzzle
B. Blanket or plywood board (cut to fit your dog and your car)

III. **First Aid**
A. Keep the dog quiet and restrict all activity. See a veterinarian as soon as possible.
B. When you are moving your dog (as directed in C below), if the dog is in pain, you may wish to use a muzzle to prevent being bitten. Even a friendly dog may bite in reaction to pain. However, use a muzzle only if the dog is not having difficulty breathing and has not been vomiting. If at any time the dog has difficulty breathing, remove the muzzle. Also, do not use a muzzle if your dog has a flat face (e.g., a pug, boxer, English bulldog, etc.).
C. If your dog is unable to walk, obtain a plywood board to use as a stretcher. Slide the dog onto the board, taking care to move the pet as little as possible. Improper movement could cause severe damage, including paralysis or death.
D. Ideally, place the plywood board with the dog on it into your

vehicle. If the board will not fit, slide the dog off the board and onto the seat with as little movement of the pet as possible.

E. Pack blankets around the dog to keep the pet warm. If you are concerned that the dog may slide off the seat onto the floor, pack the floor area with a pillow or blankets. If injury is severe, treat for shock by placing one or two 2-liter soda bottles filled with warm water (not hot) against the dog. See pages 79-80.

SMOKE INHALATION

Smoke inhalation is often the cause of death when a dog is trapped in a fire. Smoke damages the respiratory tract, thereby interfering with normal breathing; in addition, smoke contains the deadly gas carbon monoxide. It is important to note that the symptoms of smoke inhalation might not appear for as long as 1 to 2 days after the exposure.

I. Symptoms (some or all may be present)
A. Difficult breathing – short, shallow or rapid breaths, panting or coughing
B. Purple, blue or pale gums and tongue
C. Disorientation
D. Coma
E. Death

II. First Aid Materials
A. 2-liter soda bottle

III. First Aid
A. Move the dog away from the smoke.
B. Check for breathing. You should be able to see the dog's chest rise and fall.
C. If the dog is not breathing, perform CPR as directed on pages 18-19.
D. Avoid all stress. The least amount of stress may precipitate a crisis when the dog is having difficulty breathing.
E. Do not monitor vital signs.
F. Plan the handling of the dog to minimize excitement. Never hold the dog tightly.
G. Keep the dog in an upright position (i.e., belly down). Never lay the dog on its back or side because those positions make

breathing more difficult by putting extra pressure on the chest.
H. Fill a 2-liter soda bottle with warm (not hot) water and place it against the dog. See illustration on page 80.
I. Contact a veterinarian immediately. It is easy to underestimate the severity of the dog's condition. Some symptoms might not appear until 12 to 48 hours after smoke inhalation occurs.

SNAIL BAIT – see page 101.

SNAKE BITES

I. Symptoms (some or all may be present)
A. Poisonous snake bites often appear as two punctures on the skin.
B. Nonpoisonous snake bites are often shaped like a "U" because nonpoisonous snakes tend to have many teeth.
C. Poisonous snake bites tend to be especially painful.
D. The site of a poisonous bite will swell and may show bruising.
E. The dog may become depressed, paralyzed, comatose, and may die. These symptoms may be preceded by respiratory distress or by digestive upset.

II. First-Aid Materials
A. Antibiotic ointment (e.g., Polysporin®)

III. First Aid
A. If you suspect that the bite is from a poisonous snake (see the symptoms listed above),
    (1) Restrict activity, and keep the dog calm. If possible, carry the dog to help. Walking can increase the circulation of poisons.
    (2) Rush the dog to a veterinarian.
B. If you suspect that the bite is from a nonpoisonous snake,
    (1) Wash the bite wound with soap and water, and then apply antibiotic ointment.
    (2) Seek veterinary care immediately. The bite could be from a poisonous snake, and even if it is not, your dog may need antibiotic therapy because reptiles have many infectious bacteria in their mouths.

SPIDER BITES, ANT BITES AND SCORPION STINGS

Note that some symptoms from spiders, ants and scorpions may not appear until 3 or 4 days after the bites or sting. These delayed symptoms may include paleness, blood in urine, fever, vomiting and shock.

I. Symptoms (some or all may be present)
A. Salivation, if bite or sting is in the dog's mouth
B. Irritated area on skin
C. Open sore on body
D. Painful area
E. Muscle pain
F. Muscle contractions
G. Fever
H. Rapid or difficult breathing
I. Paleness
J. Vomiting
K. Blood in urine
L. Shock
M. Paralysis
N. Death

II. First-Aid Materials
A. Ice
B. Towel

III. First Aid
A. Seek veterinary care immediately.
B. Restrict activity.
C. Apply antibiotic ointment.
D. If possible, identify the spider, ants or scorpion (to aid in proper veterinary care).

STRAINING

I. Problems/Conditions with that Symptom
A. Urinary tract irritation or infection

B. Urinary blockage
C. Constipation
D. Colitis
E. Difficult delivery

II. First-Aid Materials
A. 2-liter soda bottle

III. First Aid
A. Observe the dog for urine output. The dog should be able to excrete at least small amounts of urine. If no urine production is detected, it is a life-threatening emergency because the dog may be blocked and unable to urinate.
B. If you suspect urinary blockage, proceed as follows:
(1) Contact a veterinarian immediately.
(2) Avoid lifting the dog around its abdomen (to avoid discomfort and possible rupture of the bladder).
(3) Keep the dog warm by placing a 2-liter soda bottle filled with warm water (not hot water) against the dog.
(4) Do not encourage the dog to eat or drink because your veterinarian may determine that a urinary catheter is necessary, and insertion of the catheter may require a general anesthetic.
C. Other signs of a urinary tract problem include frequent attempted urination and crying during urination. Even if urine is being produced, if you suspect a urinary tract problem, consult a veterinarian as soon as possible for diagnosis and treatment before the situation turns into a life-threatening block.
D. If a urinary tract irritation and blockage can be ruled out, see the sections on constipation (page 40), colitis (page 38) and deliveries (pages 41-42).

STRANGULATION

If your dog wears a collar that is not a break-away collar, there is a danger that the collar could become caught on something (e.g., a tree branch, a fence, or another dog's mouth). Sometimes the tags on a collar become wedged in vents, between deck boards, or anywhere that the tags will fit through only one way. The result could be strangulation.

I. First-Aid Materials
A. Scissors, tree trimmer, and or bolt cutter

II. First Aid
A. If the dog is conscious, free the collar or cut it off.
B. If the dog is not conscious:
   (1) Free the collar or cut it off as quickly as possible.
   (2) Perform CPR as directed on pages 18-19.

STRYCHNINE POISONING – see page 101.

TIGHT COLLAR

If your dog is still growing or is gaining weight, its collar may become too tight. The collar could cause difficulty breathing and it could actually cut into the skin.

I. Symptoms (some or all may be present)
A. Dog scratching/pawing at its neck
B. Difficulty breathing
C. Bloody discharge or putrid smell from collar area

II. First-Aid Materials
A. Antibiotic ointment (e.g., Polysporin®)
B. Scissors

III. First Aid
A. If the collar has not grown into the skin, simply loosen it or remove it.
B. If the collar has grown into the skin:
   (1) Clip hair away from the collar.
   (2) Try to find a place where you can gently slip the scissors under the collar to cut it off. If you are unsuccessful, seek veterinary assistance to have the collar removed.
   (3) Apply antibiotic ointment to the wound.
   (4) Seek veterinary care to treat for possible infection.

TOAD POISONING

Many toads produce venom from glands in their skin. The amount of venom and its potency can vary greatly.

I. Symptoms (some or all may be present)
A. Salivation
B. Rubbing mouth
C. Shaking head
D. Dry heaves
E. Vomiting
F. Weakness
G. Difficulty breathing
H. Blue gums
I. Seizures
J. Collapse
K. Death

II. First-Aid Materials
A. Fresh water
B. Eyedropper or dosage syringe

III. First Aid
A. Using an eyedropper or dosage syringe, flush the dog's mouth with fresh water to remove excess venom.
B. If possible, identify the type of toad.
C. Seek veterinary care.

TOENAIL EMERGENCIES

It is important to keep your dog's toenails trimmed to prevent them from catching on carpets and outdoor hazards.

I. Symptoms (some or all may be present)
A. Lameness
B. Nail hanging from paw
C. Blood coming from nail bed
D. Dog shaking its paw

II. First-Aid Materials
A. Muzzle
B. Nonstick bandages and gauze wrap

C. Tape
D. Nail trimmers

III. First Aid
A. Apply a muzzle if there is no evidence of difficulty breathing or nausea. If at any time the dog has difficulty breathing, remove the muzzle. Also, do not use a muzzle if your dog has a flat face (e.g., a pug, boxer, English bulldog, etc.).
B. Do not attempt to remove a dangling nail. (You may, however, trim the nail to help prevent further injury to the nail bed.) If the paw is bleeding, apply gentle but firm pressure to the paw to stop the bleeding.
C. If the bleeding persists, wrap the foot using a nonstick bandage, gauze wrap and tape. (See Wrapping a Wound on page 16.)
D. See a veterinarian to have the nail trimmed or removed and for treatment to prevent infection.
E. Keep the dog's healthy toenails trimmed to prevent injuries in the future.

URINARY TRACT IRRITATIONS

Urinary tract irritations may be caused by a variety of problems including infections and bladder or kidney stones. In the worst-case scenario, a dog may be unable to urinate because of a blockage. If the blockage is left untreated, death is imminent.

I. Symptoms (some or all may be present)
A. Broken house habits (i.e., urinating in the house)
B. Urinating more frequently
C. Straining while trying to urinate
D. Crying while urinating
E. Blood in the urine
F. Inability to urinate
G. Other generalized signs of illness (i.e., changes in behavior)

II. First-Aid Materials
A. 2-liter soda bottle

III. First Aid
A. Observe the dog for urine output. The dog should be able to excrete at least small amounts of urine.

B. If no urine production is detected, the situation is urgent; the dog's urinary system may be blocked, and blockage is always life-threatening. Contact a veterinarian immediately.
C. Monitor the dog's vital signs. See page 17.
D. If you suspect a blockage, treat for shock. See pages 79-80.
E. Avoid lifting the dog around its abdomen (to avoid discomfort and possible rupture of the bladder).
F. Even if urine is being produced, consult a veterinarian as soon as possible for diagnosis and treatment before the situation turns into a life-threatening blockage.
G. Do not allow the dog to eat or drink if you suspect a blockage; your veterinarian may need to insert a urinary catheter, and insertion of the catheter may require a general anesthetic.

UTERUS INFECTION/PYOMETRA

Infections of the uterus can be fatal. The cause is generally hormonal. The unspayed, older adult female is at highest risk. The infection can spread through the bloodstream, or sometimes the organ will burst, spilling infection into the abdomen.

I. **Symptoms (some or all may be present)**
A. Increased thirst that precedes other signs
B. General signs of illness such as loss of appetite, vomiting, diarrhea or depression
C. A cloudy, foul-smelling discharge coming from the vulvar area under the tail
D. Tense and distended abdomen

II. **First-Aid Materials**
A. 2-liter soda bottle

III. **First Aid**
A. If any of these symptoms are noted, contact a veterinarian immediately. The dog may require an emergency spay before the uterus ruptures.
B. Do not lift the dog by putting extra pressure on the abdomen; lifting in that manner may cause the uterus to rupture.
C. To help prevent shock, place a 2-liter soda bottle filled with warm water (not hot water) next to the dog (as illustrated on page 80).

VOMITING

I. Accompanying Symptoms (some or all may be present)
A. Loss of appetite
B. Salivation
C. Retching
D. Painful abdomen

II. Problems/Conditions with that Symptom
A. Infections
B. Dietary change (e.g., different dog food, table scraps, bones, garbage)
C. Poisonings
D. Heat stroke
E. Hydroadrenocorticism (Addison's disease)
F. Shock
G. Foreign objects
H. Organ failure
I. Stress (e.g., environmental change)

III. First-Aid Materials
A. Boiled hamburger and plain cooked rice

IV. First Aid
A. Withhold food and water for 2-4 hours. (But if your dog has diabetes or any other type of illness or medical condition, consult your veterinarian first before withholding food and water.) Do not withhold food and water from a puppy or elderly dog for more than 2 hours. If symptoms persist, worsen or return within this 2-4 hour period, contact your veterinarian.
B. Note the frequency and substance of the vomiting.
C. Note how long after a meal the vomiting occurred.
D. When you do resume feeding your dog, prepare a 50/50 mixture of boiled hamburger (drain off the water and fat) and plain cooked rice. Appropriate feedings are as follows:
    (1) 1/4 cup of the mixture 4 times per day for small dogs,
    (2) 1/2 cup of the mixture 4 times per day for medium dogs,
    (3) 3/4 cup of the mixture 4 times per day for large dogs.
    Your veterinarian may wish to adjust the servings or may recommend a prescription diet instead.
E. Resume normal feeding within 2 days.

WEAKNESS/DEPRESSION

Weakness and depression are symptoms associated with many diseases and conditions. When a dog is depressed, it has a decreased response to external stimuli and a decreased interest in its surroundings. Recognizing the symptoms is easy, but pinpointing the cause is difficult. Weakness and depression are often early symptoms of a more serious problem. Consult a veterinarian early to prevent a crisis.

I. **Problems/Conditions with that Symptom**
A. Heart disease
B. Lung disease
C. Heat stroke
D. Internal bleeding
E. Shock
F. Trauma (physical injury)
G. Anemia
H. Fractured ribs
I. Poisoning
J. Asthma
K. Dehydration
L. Hypoadrenocorticism (Addison's disease)
M. Diabetes
N. Hypoglycemia (low blood sugar)
O. Liver or kidney disease

II. **First-Aid Materials**
A. Two 2-liter soda bottles
B. Blanket
C. Thermometer

III. **First Aid**
A. Keep the dog calm. Do not use excessive restraint or cause excessive movement.
B. Monitor the dog's vital signs (temperature, pulse, respirations).
C. Keep the dog warm with a blanket and with the 2-liter soda bottles filled with warm water placed close to the dog's body.
D. Call your veterinarian.

WETTING IN THE HOUSE

I. Problems/Conditions with that Symptom
A. Urinary tract irritation or infection
B. Urinary blockage
C. Metabolic changes (e.g., from diabetes or Cushing's disease)

II. First-Aid Materials
A. 2-liter soda bottle

III. First Aid
A. Observe the dog for urine output. The dog should be able to excrete at least small amounts of urine. If no urine production is detected, it is a life-threatening emergency because the dog may be blocked and unable to urinate.
B. If you suspect urinary blockage, proceed as follows:
   (1) Contact a veterinarian immediately.
   (2) Avoid lifting the dog around its abdomen (to avoid discomfort and possible rupture of the bladder).
   (3) Keep the dog warm by placing a 2-liter soda bottle filled with warm water (not hot water) against the dog.
   (4) Do not encourage the dog to eat or drink because your veterinarian may determine that a urinary catheter is necessary, and insertion of the catheter may require a general anesthetic.
C. Other signs of a urinary tract problem include straining, frequent attempted urination and crying during urination. Even if urine is being produced, if you suspect that there is a urinary tract problem, consult a veterinarian as soon as possible for diagnosis and treatment before the situation turns into a life-threatening block.

YARD CHEMICALS – see page 102.

POISON BASICS

GENERAL PROCEDURES

Because some poisons are sweet to the taste and because of the inherent curiosity of most dogs, poisons pose a substantial risk to your pet. Early recognition is critical to prevent complications or death.

I. Information About the Dog
A. Be ready to provide the following information to your veterinarian: owner's name, address and phone number and the dog's breed, age, sex and weight.
B. If you have more than one pet, note whether the others are affected.
C. Be able to describe the symptoms the dog is experiencing.

II. Information About the Exposure
A. Note the suspected substance.
B. Identify the substance ingested. Save the label or container of the suspected agent, if applicable. If the agent is a plant and cannot be identified, obtain a sample of the plant.
C. Note the time of exposure.
D. Note the amount of the substance ingested.

III. Steps to Get Help
A. Immediately contact the dog's veterinarian to see if treatment is necessary.
B. If you cannot reach a veterinarian, call a local poison control hotline or the ASPCA Animal Poison Control Center for information. (The ASPCA Animal Poison Control Center provides assistance for a fee – $50 at the time of this printing: 1-800-548-2423.)
C. Follow the veterinarian's or the Center's recommendations.
D. If you need to induce vomiting, see page 18.
E. Observe for symptoms (vomiting, diarrhea, loss of coordination, lethargy, etc.). Symptoms may not be evident immediately.

COMMON POISONS

Acids*
Alkalis*
Antidandruff shampoos
Antifreeze
Antipsychotics
Atropine
Benzodiazepines
Borates
Camphor
Chocolate*
Coal tar
Creosote
DEET
Drain cleaners
Ethylene glycol
Flea products*
Glue
Insulin
Ivermectin
Limonene
Metaldehyde
Methylxanthines
Narcotic analgesics
Petroleum distillates*
Phenylpropanolamine
Propranolol
Rat poison*
Strychnine*
Terbutaline
2,4-D
Yard chemicals*

Adhesives
Amphetamines
Antidepressants
Antihistamines
Arsenic*
Barbiturates
Bleach
Bromethalin
Chlorinated hydrocarbons
Cholecalciferol
Cocaine
Cyanide
Detergents
Ethanol
5-fluorouracil
4-animopyridine
Ibuprofen*
Isopropanol
Lead*
Mercury
Methanol
Naphthaline
PCP
Phenols
Pine oil
Pyrethrins
Snail bait*
1080
THC
Xanthines
Zinc oxide

*See below for more details.

NOTE: The above list does not include all poisons. Some substances that are not harmful to people are poisonous to dogs. Many common household products contain chemicals that are poisonous to dogs. It is reasonable to assume that anything that is poisonous to people is likely poisonous to dogs. For toxic plants, see pages 103-104.

ACIDS AND ALKALIS – Acids and alkalis are in a wide variety of products. Acids include sulfuric (in auto batteries, metal cleaners and polishes), hydrochloric (in metal cleaners and polishes), nitric (in permanent wave neutralizer), oxalic (in cleaning solutions, bleach, and furniture and floor polishes and waxes), carbolic acid or phenol (in antiseptics and disinfectants). Alkalis include sodium hydroxide/lye (in aquarium products, drain cleaners and small batteries), potassium hydroxide (in cuticle remover and some small batteries), sodium phosphate (in abrasive cleaners), sodium carbonate (in dye removers and dishwasher soap). There are also alkalis in ammonia and bleaches. With acid or alkali ingestion, **do NOT induce vomiting**.

I. **Symptoms**
A. Salivating
B. Vomiting
C. Diarrhea
D. Weakness

II. **First-Aid Materials**
A. Milk of Magnesia®
B. Lemon juice
C. Vinegar
D. Baking soda
E. Eyedropper or dosage syringe

III. **First Aid**
A. **Do not induce vomiting**.
B. **For acid ingestion**, feed your dog 1 tablespoon Milk of Magnesia® using an eyedropper or dosage syringe.
C. **For acid burns**, flush areas with copious amounts of water. Then apply a paste of 1 part baking soda to 2 parts water.
D. **For alkali ingestion**,
    (1) Mix 1 teaspoon vinegar with 4 teaspoons water, and feed the mixture to your dog using an eyedropper or dosage syringe, **or**
    (2) Feed your dog 1 tablespoon lemon juice using an eyedropper or dosage syringe. (You may mix 1 teaspoon of sugar into the lemon juice so that the dog will like it better.)
E. **For alkali burns**, flush the areas with copious amounts of water. Apply a solution of 1 cup vinegar to 4 cups water over areas.
F. Contact a veterinarian for additional instructions.

ARSENIC POISONING – Arsenic poisoning can occur in dogs that ingest water or plants that have been contaminated with herbicides or pesticides containing arsenic. If your dog does ingest arsenic, early treatment is essential because arsenic is extremely toxic.

I. Symptoms (some or all may be present)
A. Abdominal pain
B. Weakness
C. Salivating
D. Vomiting
E. Diarrhea
F. Shaking
G. Staggering
H. Collapse
I. Death

II. First-Aid Materials
A. Hydrogen peroxide
B. Eyedropper or dosage syringe
C. Raw egg whites

III. First Aid
A. If an exposure is suspected, induce vomiting by feeding the dog 1 teaspoon of hydrogen peroxide (mixed with 1 teaspoon milk if available). If the dog will not drink the mixture or if there is no milk available, then force-feed the dog the hydrogen peroxide using an eyedropper or dosage syringe. If vomiting does not occur within 10 minutes, repeat the procedure up to two times.
B. Get immediate veterinary help.
C. If a veterinarian cannot be found, then when vomiting ceases or if vomiting cannot be induced, use an eyedropper to slowly feed the dog 2 tablespoons of raw egg whites.

CHOCOLATE TOXICITY – Chocolate contains a substance called theobromine which cannot be readily metabolized by dogs. Even in small quantities, chocolate may be toxic to your dog.

I. Symptoms (some or all may be present)
A. Moderate to severe vomiting and diarrhea
B. Excitability and nervousness

C. Muscle tremors and/or seizures

D. Heart failure

II. First-Aid Materials

A. Hydrogen peroxide

B. Eyedropper or dosage syringe

III. First Aid

A. If the ingestion has occurred within the previous 6 hours, immediately induce vomiting by feeding the dog 1 teaspoon of hydrogen peroxide (mixed with 1 teaspoon milk if available). If the dog will not drink the mixture or if there is no milk available, then force-feed the dog the hydrogen peroxide using an eyedropper. If vomiting does not occur within 10 minutes, repeat the procedure twice.

B. See a veterinarian for further monitoring and supportive care.

FLEA PRODUCT TOXICITY – Dogs sometimes have reactions to flea products. Follow the flea-product directions to minimize the risk to your dog. If the product is new to your dog, observe your dog after you use the product to make sure that there is no adverse reaction. The relatively small risk associated with using flea products is justified, however, because fleas can spread parasites and infections, and they can cause fatal anemia.

I. Symptoms

A. Drooling longer than 20 minutes

B. Loss of appetite

C. Digestive upset

D. Seizures or muscle tremors (in severe cases)

E. Disorientation

II. First-Aid Materials

A. Shampoo that does not contain flea chemicals

III. First Aid

A. If chemicals have been applied to the dog, immediately wash off the product using shampoo and water. Repeat once.

B. See a veterinarian for an antidote, further monitoring, and supportive care.

IBUPROFEN TOXICITY – Ibuprofen (e.g., Advil®) is an anti-inflammatory drug that, for dogs, is very toxic. Some ibuprofen brands are sugar-coated and appeal to dogs. Human medications should never be given to pets without the advice of a veterinarian.

I. Symptoms (some or all may be present)
A. Digestive upset
B. Bloody stool
C. Depression
D. Staggering
E. Increased thirst
F. Increased frequency of urination
G. Liver disease
H. Kidney disease
I. Seizures

II. First-Aid Materials
A. Hydrogen peroxide
B. Eyedropper or dosage syringe

III. First Aid
A. If the pet is conscious, induce vomiting immediately by feeding the dog 1 teaspoon of hydrogen peroxide (mixed with 1 teaspoon of milk if available). If the dog will not drink the mixture or if there is no milk available, then force-feed the dog the hydrogen peroxide using an eyedropper or dosage syringe. If vomiting does not occur within 10 minutes, repeat the procedure twice.
B. Contact your veterinarian for further treatment regardless of whether you have been successful at inducing vomiting.

LEAD TOXICITY – Lead poisoning is becoming less common because of an increased awareness of its health hazards. Lead poisoning is seen more commonly in dogs than in cats because dogs tend to chew extraneous objects to a greater extent than do cats. Products like paint, plaster, caulking, linoleum, solder, improperly glazed dishes, fishing sinkers and golf balls sometimes contain lead.

I. Symptoms
A. Digestive upset
B. Loss of appetite

C. Personality/behavior change
D. Seizures and blindness (in severe cases)

II. First-Aid Materials
A. Hydrogen peroxide
B. Eyedropper
C. Raw egg white

III. First Aid
A. If the ingestion has occurred within the last 6 hours, immediately induce vomiting by feeding the dog 1 teaspoon of hydrogen peroxide (mixed with 1 teaspoon milk if available). If the dog will not drink the mixture or if there is no milk available, then force-feed the dog the hydrogen peroxide using an eyedropper. If vomiting does not occur within 10 minutes, repeat the procedure twice.
B. After vomiting has stopped, or if you are unsuccessful at inducing vomiting, mix 1 raw egg white with 2 cups of water. Encourage the dog to drink as much of this solution as possible, or slowly administer 1/2 cup (for small dogs) up to 2 cups (for a large dog) with an eyedropper or dosage syringe.
C. See a veterinarian for further monitoring and supportive care.

PETROLEUM DISTILLATES – Petroleum distillates include gasoline, kerosene, paint thinner, lighter fluid, mineral spirits, diesel fuel, some household all-purpose lubricating oils (e.g., WD-40® and 3-IN-ONE® household oil) and petroleum-based insecticides (e.g., Raid®). Some furniture polishes and cleaners also contain petroleum distillates. If ingestion of petroleum distillates does occur, **do not induce vomiting.** Vomiting may cause the petroleum to become aspirated (i.e., breathed into the lungs), which will cause respiratory irritations and possibly pneumonia.

I. Symptoms (some or all may be present)
A. Salivation
B. Odor of petroleum
C. Difficulty breathing

II. First-Aid Materials
A. Any vegetable oil
B. Eyedropper or dosage syringe

III. First Aid
A. Feed the dog 1-2 tablespoons of vegetable oil using an eyedropper or dosage syringe.
B. Contact a veterinarian immediately.

RAT POISON – Rat poisons are laced in a grain base which intrigues dogs. When a dog eats rat poison, the poison interferes with the dog's ability to make vitamin K. Vitamin K is essential in causing blood to clot, and without the vitamin, a dog will hemorrhage internally. Because the symptoms from rat poison take several days to appear, early treatment is essential if an exposure is even suspected.

I. Symptoms (some or all may be present)
A. None for several days
B. Weakness – frequently the first symptom
C. Pale, white or bruised gums
D. Bruises on the dog's body
E. Bloody urine and/or stools
F. Blue-green feces or vomitus – some rat baits contain a blue-green dye
G. Death – may occur within 24 hours of first symptoms

II. First-Aid Materials
A. Hydrogen peroxide
B. Eyedropper or dosage syringe

III. First Aid
A. If exposure has occurred within 6 hours, immediately induce vomiting by feeding the dog 1 teaspoon of hydrogen peroxide (mixed with 1 teaspoon of milk if available). If the dog will not drink the mixture or if there is no milk available, then force-feed the dog the hydrogen peroxide using an eyedropper or dosage syringe. If vomiting does not occur within 10 minutes, repeat the procedure twice.
B. Regardless of whether you have been able to induce vomiting, seek veterinary care immediately. Your veterinarian will prescribe vitamin K as an antidote and may also prescribe medicines to slow absorption of the poison.

SNAIL BAIT – Snail bait is poisonous to pets because it contains the chemical metaldehyde. This product, like rat poison, is made with a tasty base that attracts not only snails but also dogs.

I. Symptoms
A. Loss of coordination
B. Muscle tremors or convulsions
C. Increased heart rate

II. First-Aid Materials
A. Hydrogen peroxide
B. Eyedropper or dosage syringe

III. First Aid
A. Induce vomiting if exposure is suspected. (Do not attempt to induce vomiting if the pet exhibits any loss of coordination or is having a seizure; the pet could aspirate vomit into its lungs.) Induce vomiting by feeding the dog 1 teaspoon of hydrogen peroxide (mixed with 1 teaspoon of milk if available). If the dog will not drink the mixture or if there is no milk available, then force-feed the dog the hydrogen peroxide using an eyedropper or dosage syringe. If vomiting does not occur within 10 minutes, repeat the procedure twice.
B. Contact a veterinarian immediately.

STRYCHNINE POISONING – Strychnine is sometimes an ingredient in products sold to kill insects and rodents. Strychnine is highly poisonous, and even a small amount will likely kill your dog. If your dog does ingest strychnine, immediate action is necessary.

I. Symptoms
A. Symptoms may appear within 2 hours of ingestion.
B. The dog may appear to be apprehensive or nervous.
C. Stiffness may develop, leading to severe seizures. These seizures can be provoked or exacerbated by external stimuli (e.g., noise, trauma, etc.).
D. Exhaustion and death may shortly follow the onset of symptoms.

II. First-Aid Materials
A. Hydrogen peroxide
B. Eyedropper or dosage syringe

III. First Aid

A. If the pet is conscious and alert, immediately induce vomiting by feeding the dog 1 teaspoon of hydrogen peroxide (mixed with 1 teaspoon of milk if available). If the dog will not drink the mixture or if there is no milk available, then force-feed the dog the hydrogen peroxide using an eyedropper or dosage syringe. If vomiting does not occur within 10 minutes, repeat the procedure twice.

B. To keep your dog from injuring itself during a seizure, block off access to stairways and move any objects or furniture that may cause injury. If a seizure does occur, refer to pages 78-79.

C. Keep the dog in a quiet environment.

D. Seek veterinary help.

YARD CHEMICALS – A variety of chemicals in fertilizers and pesticides can cause illness either from inhalation, contact or ingestion. Symptoms of illness may be delayed for days, but may be quite severe. Avoid exposing your dog to these toxins by keeping your dog indoors during and immediately after yard fertilization and spraying, and if you are using an insecticide indoors, keep your dog out of the room until the chemicals have dissipated. Never spray your dog with an insecticide that is not labeled specifically for use on dogs.

I. Symptoms (some or all may be present)

A. Listlessness

B. Loss of appetite

C. Difficulty breathing

D. Vomiting

E. Diarrhea

F. Skin irritation from contact (typically the pads of the feet)

II. First Aid Materials

A. Shampoo

III. First Aid

A. If the dog gets chemicals on its fur, bathe the dog with dog shampoo (or any mild moisturizing shampoo if dog shampoo is not available). While restraining the dog, apply the shampoo and let it stand for 10 minutes before rinsing well.

B. Seek veterinary assistance for additional advice and treatment.

INGESTION OF TOXIC PLANTS

If your dog has ingested a suspected toxic substance, your best bet is to contact a poison-control center immediately. The ASPCA Animal Poison Control Center provides assistance for a fee ($50 at the time of this printing): 1-800-548-2423. There might also be a local poison-control hotline where you live.

Many plant poisonings require quick home treatment followed by immediate veterinary care. Veterinary follow-up is critical to prevent secondary effects of the poisons. Also, a veterinarian can monitor the dog for complications.

It is important to note that because of the huge number of plants in existence, this section of this book cannot possibly address every plant that is or may be toxic to dogs. Also, some plants that are generally considered to be nontoxic may cause severe symptoms in a dog with an allergy to the plant. And some plants that are not toxic are sprayed with chemicals that may be poisonous. Therefore, you should be concerned whenever your dog eats any type of plant, and you should contact your veterinarian immediately. To the extent possible, keep all plants out of the reach of your pet.

If you do not recognize a plant that your dog has ingested, obtain a sample that is identifiable (e.g., a complete plant, a leaf, etc.). Many plants can be identified by veterinarians, and veterinarians frequently have plant reference books to aid in identification.

Some of the most toxic varieties of plants include the following:
1. Philodendron species
2. Dieffenbachia species
3. Solanum species
4. Ranunculus species
5. Helleborous species
6. Clematis species
7. Digitalis species
8. Nerium oleander
9. Rhododendron species
10. Convallaria majalis
11. Prunus

If your pet has ingested any type of plant, contact a veterinarian or a poison control center right away. Do not wait for symptoms to develop.

The following is a list of ten surprising facts about plants that are toxic to dogs:

1. Grapes and raisins can be toxic to some dogs and can cause acute kidney failure.
2. Some parts of edible plants can be toxic. For example, the leaves and stems of apples and cherries contain cyanide.
3. All parts of the Easter lily are poisonous. Every year many pet deaths are the result of kidney failure from ingestion of Easter lilies.
4. The ingestion of one castor bean can be fatal.
5. Yews contain alkaloids, and all parts but the red berry are toxic.
6. All parts of azaleas are toxic, and ingestion can result in symptoms ranging from a digestive upset to coma and death.
7. Morning glory ingestion can cause your dog digestive upset and hallucinations.
8. Onion ingestion can cause hemolytic anemia in dogs.
9. One leaf or seed from the snow-on-the-mountain plant can be deadly.
10. The tuber portion of water hemlock can cause seizures.

NONTOXIC PLANTS

I.   Warning
A.   Even though many plants are not toxic, when ingested in large quantity they can cause digestive upset. Also, even plants that are generally not considered to be poisonous can cause an allergic reaction that may be serious. Each dog is unique, and a plant that may cause no difficulties for one dog may be toxic for another.

II.   Special Considerations
A.   Plants may be sprayed with chemicals which can be toxic to dogs.
B.   Often a dog will eat plants, especially grass, when the dog feels ill from something else. Grass, although not harmful, usually causes the dog to vomit. If your dog is eating plants or grass, observe for other signs of illness, and consult your veterinarian.

PLANTS THAT CAUSE SKIN IRRITATION

There are two types of skin irritation caused by plants. The first is irritation caused by a reaction to the chemicals in the plant (usually in the plant's sap or resin). Examples include asparagus fern, chrysanthemum resin, manchineel sap, poinsettia sap and primrose leaves. The second type of skin irritation occurs from certain types of grasses (e.g., foxtail/grass awns) when tiny parts of the plant (spikelets) become embedded in and under the dog's skin (e.g., in the ears or in the webbing of the feet). If the plant spikelets are not removed, they may cause abscesses (i.e., infections). Your veterinarian may need to sedate your dog in order to remove the spikelets.

I. List of Plants

A. Asparagus fern
B. Chrysanthemum resin
C. Manchineel sap
D. Poinsettia sap
E. Primrose leaves
F. Foxtail/grass awns

II. First Aid

A. For everything except foxtail/grass awns, wash affected area with soap and water and cleanse with alcohol.
B. For foxtail/grass awns:
    (1) Apply antibiotic ointment (e.g., Polysporin®) to the affected area.
    (2) If the dog persistently licks or scratches the affected area, apply an Elizabethan collar. See page 21.
    (3) Contact your veterinarian for removal of spikelets or for more information.

BIBLIOGRAPHY

Alber, John I., and Delores M. Alber. *Baby-Safe Houseplants & Cut Flowers*. Highland, IL: Genus Books, 1991.

Arthurs, Kathryn, ed. *How to Grow House Plants*. 2nd ed. Menlo Park: Lane Publishing, 1974.

Davis, Lloyd E., *Handbook of Small Animal Therapeutics*. Liningston, NY: Churchill, 1985.

Fenner, William R., D.V.M., ed. *Quick Reference to Veterinary Medicine*. 2nd ed. Philadelphia: J.P. Lippincott, 1991.

Florists' Transworld Delivery Association. *Professional Guide to Green Plants*. Florists' Transworld Delivery Association, 1976.

Fowler, Murray E., D.V.M. *Plant Poisoning in Small Companion Animals*. St. Louis: Ralston Purina, 1981.

Fraser, Clarence M., ed. *The Merck Veterinary Manual*. 6th, 7th ed. Rathway, NJ: Merck & Co., 1986, 1991.

Hoskins, Johnny D. *Veterinary Pediatrics: Dogs and Cats from Birth to Six Months*. Philadelphia: W. B. Saunders, 1990.

Kirk, Robert W., D.V.M., and Stephen I. Bister, D.V.M. *Handbook of Veterinary Procedures and Emergency Treatment*. 4th ed. Philadelphia: W. B. Saunders, 1985.

Levy, Charles Kingsley, and Richard B. Primack. *A Field Guide to Poisonous Plants and Mushrooms of North America*. Brattleboro, VT: The Stephen Greene Press, 1984.

Muller, George H., Robert W. Kirk, and Danny W. Scott. *Small Animal Dermatololgy*. 3rd ed. Philadelphia: W. B. Saunders, 1983.

National Animal Poison Control Center. *Household Plant List*. Urbana: University of Illinois College of Veterinary Medicine.

Osweiler, Gary D., D.V.M., Thomas L. Carson, D.V.M., William B. Buck, D.V.M., and Gary A VanGelder, D.V.M. *Clinical and Diagnostic Veterinary Toxicology*. 3rd ed. Dubuque, IA: Kendell/Hunt, 1985.

Random House Webster's College Dictionary. New York: Random House, 1991.

Taylor, Norman. *Taylor's Guide to Perennials*. Ed. Gordon P. DeWolf. Boston: Houghton Mifflin, 1961.

Tuckington, Carol. *The Home Health Guide to Poisons and Antidotes*. New York: Facts on File, 1994.

Woodward, Lucia. *Poisonous Plants: A Color Field Guide*. New York: Hippocrene Books, 1985.

INDEX

108

112

Emergency First Aid For Your Dog

Handbook

Dr. Tamara S. Shearer
Edited by Stanford Apseloff